The Ultimate Scene Study Series
for Teens Volume I

SIXTY
SHAKESPEARE
SCENES

Edited by Lisa Bansavage,
L. E. McCullough, and Jill K. Swanson

YOUNG ACTORS SERIES

A Smith and Kraus Book

A Smith and Kraus Book
Published by Smith and Kraus, Inc.
177 Lyme Road, Hanover, NH 03755
smithandkraus.com

First Edition: May 2003
Manufactured in the United States of America
8 7 6 5 4 3 2 1

Cover and text design by Julia Gignoux, Freedom Hill Design

Library of Congress Cataloging-in-Publication Data
Shakespeare, William, 1564–1616.
[Plays. Selections]
Sixty Shakespeare scenes for teens / [compiled] by Lisa Bansavage, L. E.
McCullough, and Jill K. Swanson. —1st ed.
p. cm. — (Young actors series)
Contents: Scenes with two characters — Scenes with three characters —
Scenes with four characters — Scenes with five or more characters.
ISBN 1-57525-359-3 / ISBN-13: 978-1-57525-359-6
1. Shakespeare, William, 1564–1616—Adaptations. 2. Yound adult
drama, English. [1. Shakespeare, William 1564–1616—Adaptations. 2.
Acting. 3. English drama—17th century.] I. Title: 60 Shakespeare scenes
for teens. II. Bansavage, Lisa. III. McCullough, L. E. IV. Swanson, Jill K.
V. Title. VI. Young actors series.

PR2877.S5 2003
822.3'3—dc21
2003042784

To actors everywhere who help us see
"the cloud-capped towers, the gorgeous palaces,
the solemn temples, the great globe itself"

THE ULTIMATE SCENE STUDY SERIES FOR TEENS

The Ultimate Scene Study Series for Teens Volume 1:
60 Shakespeare Scenes

The Ultimate Scene Study Series for Teens Volume 2:
60 Original Scenes by Debbie Lamedman

THE ULTIMATE AUDITION BOOK FOR TEENS SERIES

The Ultimate Audition Book for Teens Volume 1: 111 One-Minute
Monologues by Janet Milstein

The Ultimate Audition Book for Teens Volume 2: 111 One-Minute
Monologues by L. E. McCullough

The Ultimate Audition Book for Teens Volume 4: 111 One-Minute
Monologues by Debbie Lamedman

The Ultimate Audition Book for Teens Volume 5:
111 Shakespeare Monologues

ACKNOWLEDGMENTS

LISA BANSAVAGE would like to acknowledge the Stratford, Ontario Shakespeare Festival for inspiring me as a teenager; Carnegie Mellon University and the conservatory training I received there; Director Patrick Tucker for awakening me to the joys of working from the First Folio; my parents, Judith and Joseph Bansavage, for exposing me as a child to great theater; Ms. Kathleen Bishop; and all the wonderful actors I've had the pleasure of performing with who share a love of Shakespeare.

JILL K. SWANSON would like to acknowledge Anne Towns; Daniel Wilson, Austin Shakespeare Festival; Jean McDaniel, Florida State University; Ann Ciccolella, Zachary Scott Theatre; Elizabeth Hansing-Moon, St. Stephen's Episcopal School; and Bill and Jeanne Swanson.

L. E. MCCULLOUGH would like to acknowledge *MacBird!* by Barbara Garson, the modern fable in Shakespearean clothing that sparked my interest in theater as a vehicle for social commentary and proved the Bard created timeless drama for every age; my parents, Isabel and Ervin McCullough, who gave me my first glimpse of theater at the old Starlight Musicals (R.I.P.); and my wife, Lisa Bansavage — the light that breaks through yonder window of my soul.

CONTENTS

SCENES FOR TWO CHARACTERS

1 MALE AND 1 FEMALE

2 MALES

2 FEMALES

SCENES FOR THREE CHARACTERS

2 FEMALES AND 1 MALE

2 MALES AND 1 FEMALE

3 MALES

SCENES FOR FOUR CHARACTERS

2 MALES AND 2 FEMALES

3 MALES AND 1 FEMALE

3 FEMALES AND 1 MALE

4 FEMALES

1 MALE, 1 FEMALE, 2 MALES OR FEMALES

SCENES FOR FIVE OR MORE CHARACTERS

5 CHARACTERS

6 CHARACTERS

7 CHARACTERS

8 CHARACTERS

12 CHARACTERS

13 CHARACTERS

INTRODUCTION

This collection of scenes is intended to give the student or new-comer to Shakespeare a chance to explore some of the well-known younger characters in his plays. The scenes are organized by the number of players involved. We have done our best to concentrate on the younger characters in Shakespeare. Occasionally, scenes will include an older character, giving you a chance to sample a more mature role. There are several scenes that have supporting roles that call for actors to be alert and in character even when they may not be speaking or have few lines.

These scenes were also chosen with regard to similar themes and situations that will encourage you to compare Shakespeare's characters. For example, there are vast differences between various "wooing scenes," if you look at Romeo and Juliet, Anne and Richard III, and Kate and Petruchio! We think you will make some exciting discoveries in these scenes.

PLAYING SHAKESPEARE

The very best way to appreciate Shakespeare's genius is by *playing* it! Merely reading the words on the page is nowhere near the experience you will enjoy once you start using the language for yourself. By saying the lines out loud, you'll see how quickly characters spring to life. All the information you need about your character has been artfully provided by Shakespeare via the construction of your lines and the words he has chosen to have the character express. Through language, your character is revealed as royal or lowborn, wise or foolish, direct or bombastic, joking or earnest, cruel or kind. When a line is simple and straightforward, the idea the character is expressing is simple and straightforward. Often, however, Shakespeare's lines are deliberately complex, expressing complex states of mind or internal conflicts in the character. Your understanding of what you are saying will increase as you learn more about the construction of the plays.

VERSE AND PROSE

The majority of Shakespeare's plays are written in verse. Some of it rhymes, much does not. The verse that does not rhyme is called *blank verse*. The name for this is *iambic pentameter*, or five sets of two stressed syllables or words. The rhythm is: de-*dum*-de-*dum*-de-*dum*-de-*dum*.

An example of iambic pentameter is Romeo's line: "But *soft*, what *light* through *yon*der *win*dow *breaks*. The stress falls on the second, fourth, sixth, eighth, and tenth syllables.

Verse is not blank when it rhymes. The use of a *rhyming couplet* or a pair of rhymed lines often punctuates the end of an important speech, the end of the scene, or the end of the play.

Prose is less formal language; free-form, like the text you are reading now. For variety, and for effect, Shakespeare chooses when characters speak in prose or verse. Part of your challenge as an actor is to be aware of whether your character is speaking in verse or prose. For instance, verse is frequently spoken by characters of higher social status. Also, a shift in speech from prose to verse can indicate an elevated emotional state. Start to look for clues about your character. Shakespeare put everything you need in the text.

For a more detailed discussion of Shakespeare's use of verse and prose, check the introduction to another Smith and Kraus book, *One Hundred Eleven Shakespeare Monologues for Teens*.

RHETORICAL ELEMENTS AND IMAGERY

What makes Shakespeare's work so remarkable is the way in which he develops his characters so clearly and realistically through brilliant choice of language. Each character has a distinctive style, a capacity for evoking a particular emotional response. He was a master of comedy, pathos, suspense, and romance — skilled at depicting human nature with impartiality. Thus, understanding Shakespeare's use of *rhetoric* (constructing speech for persuasive impact) is important in playing Shakespeare. Although the sentences can at first feel daunting to an actor with their twists and turns and flowery embellishments, a skillful performer soon learns to joyously ride the words and breath living reality into the imagery.

Elaborate descriptive detail was a very practical matter for Shakespeare, as well as a means for showing his art. Since plays were presented in daylight, usually without benefit of elaborate sets, the actors needed to paint a very clear word picture to help the audience imagine scenes and settings. Perhaps a figure of speech by a chorus would direct the audience's imagination to a battlefield of men on horseback:

> Think, when we talk of horses, that you see them
> Printing their proud hoofs in the receiving earth
>> — *Henry V*, Prologue

Another character might inform the audience that the action is at sunrise:

> But look, the morn in russet mantle clad
> Walks o'er the dew of yon high eastern hill
>> — *Hamlet*, Act I, Scene 1

John Dryden, another great English writer, remarked of Shakespeare's evocative and precise language, "When he describes anything, you more than see it, you feel it too."

STRANGE WORDS

You will encounter a fair number of strange words in Shakespeare. It is a good idea to use one of the many dictionaries available especially for Shakespeare. A good one, recently published by Smith and Kraus, is titled *All the Words on Stage: A Complete Pronunciation Dictionary for the Plays of William Shakespeare* by Louis Scheeder and Shane Ann Younts.

Some of Shakespeare's words are *archaic*, meaning that they are no longer used. Some words have changed from what they meant then to what they mean now, and some are words that Shakespeare coined that did not make it into popular use. However, a great many words he used for the first time have become a part of our everyday speech:

gloomy	hint	leapfrog	excellent	bump
lonely	tongue-tied	hoodwinked	yelping	hurry
zany	aerial	barefaced	dwindle	seamy
fretful	frugal	lackluster	majestic	tranquil

These common expressions come from Shakespeare plays: "dull as dishwater," "budge an inch," "set your teeth on edge," "one fell swoop," "melted into thin air," "the long and short of it," "the game is up." Without realizing it, you hear Shakespeare spoken every day of your life!

Fewer people could read in Shakespeare's day than now. Most people were accustomed to *listening* for their information. Today we have been conditioned to gather information visually — television, billboards, and advertising logos dominate our world. We get "soundbites," which employ a minimum number of words to give us a maximum amount of information or to stimulate a favorable response to products and services: "Just do it," "Got milk?," "Wider is better," "Supersize it!," and so forth.

When you begin to work on Shakespeare with scene partners, you'll discover the joy of sinking your teeth into some truly delectable language. When the language seems complex, it is because the character is expressing a complex state of mind. Take your time and say the lines the way Shakespeare has written them. Trust the text, and it will tell you everything you need to become the character.

With a little practice, you will begin to see the artful construction of his characters by the distinctive way each one speaks. In time, you will experience your character and your character's motives through the information Shakespeare gives you in your lines. As you continue to read the plays and work on scenes, you'll begin to see how certain patterns, imagery, or themes are reinvented for different plays. Eventually, you will develop an ear for your character's rhythms; you'll feel as though you are simply speaking as your character.

PLOTS AND SUBPLOTS

Most of Shakespeare's plots are not original. He borrowed freely from well-known stories, including a certain poem about two tragic lovers by English poet Arthur Broke titled *The Tragicall Historye of Romeus and Juliet*, based on a French translation of a tale by the fifteenth-century Italian writer Matteo Bandello. Greek and Roman mythology, Bible stories, folktales, and a history book called the *Holinshed Chronicles* were also useful fodder for this brilliant poet's pen.

Most of the plays have at least one *subplot*. The subplot of Bianca and her many suitors in *The Taming of the Shrew*, for instance, was inspired by an earlier comedy from 1566, George Gascoigne's *Supposes* (1566), which was itself a translation of *I suppositi,* published in 1509 by Ludovico Ariosto.

Although these subplots were great crowd pleasers and provided many memorable comic and dramatic supporting characters, using them was considered "breaking the rules" of good playwriting at the time. Well-wrought plays were supposed to adhere to Aristotle's standard of the Three Unities — *time, place,* and *location* — focusing on only one story through the play. Yet Shakespeare was an innovator, a writer who sought to put his own unique stamp on these timeless tales. Many scenes in this book involve subplots almost as interesting as the main plot line.

THEMES

Several scenes in this collection were chosen specifically to give you the opportunity to compare and contrast how different characters behave in similar situations. When you explore a scene, be on the lookout for other similar scenes for comparison. No matter how often Shakespeare used and reused similar ideas or themes, he gave distinctive color to each character, thereby making a fresh effect for the audience.

Above all, have fun, and know that Shakespeare's text is a bottomless treasure trove for any reader or audience and most especially for you — the actor!

LOVE

Shakespeare considered love to be a (fun) form of mental illness. Like a brain fever, it takes away all reason and leaves only chaos and raw emotion. No wonder, then, that many of Shakespeare's characters try to resist being in love or deny it to themselves and each other as they struggle to maintain their sanity. It is only young characters like Romeo and Juliet who throw themselves into it wholeheartedly, and you know what happens to them . . . they kill themselves (if you hadn't heard).

But even when older characters try to resist, they too find themselves swept away with the promise of love. Let's look at three love scenes with characters of different ages — Romeo and Juliet from *Romeo and Juliet,* Beatrice and Benedick of *Much Ado About Nothing*, and Richard and Anne from *Richard III* — and see how they are different and how they are alike.

First, let's note the *language* of love scenes. Lovers speak differently than other characters, often rhyming and playing off the words of others. In Romeo and Juliet's party scene, when their lines are put together, they make up *sonnets.* Sonnets are poems with fourteen lines; the last two always rhyme and usually make a sort of punchline to the poem. Here's an example of a Shakespeare sonnet; compare the sonnet to this dialogue from when Romeo and Juliet first meet, which leads up to their first kiss:

Sonnet 147

My love is a fever, longing still
For that which longer nurseth the disease
Feeding on that which doeth preserve the ill,
The uncertain sickly appetite to please.
My reason, the physician to my love,
Angry that his prescriptions are not kept
Hath left me, and I desperate now approve
Desire is death, which physic did accept.
Past cure I am, now reason is past care,
And frantic-mad with evermore unrest,
My thoughts and my discourse as madmen's are

At random from the truth vainly express'd.
For I have sworn thee fair and thought thee bright
Who art black as hell, as dark as night.

Now look at Romeo and Juliet's lines:

ROMEO
>   If I profane with my unworthiest hand
>   This holy shrine, the gentle fine is this:
>   My lips, two blushing pilgrims ready stand
>   To smooth that rough touch with a tender kiss.

JULIET
>   Good pilgrim, you do wrong your hand too much
>   Which mannerly devotion shows in this;
>   For saints have hands that pilgrims' hands do touch
>   And palm to palm is holy palmers' kiss.

ROMEO
>   Have not saints lips, and holy palmers too?

JULIET
>   Ay, pilgrim, lips that they must use in prayer.

ROMEO
>   O then, dear saint, let lips do what hands do
>   They pray, grant thou, lest faith turn to despair.

JULIET
>   Saints do not move, though grant for prayer's sake.

ROMEO
>   Then move not while my prayer's effect I take.

This way of speaking is meant to indicate that there is something really special happening between these two people, a joke that only they are in on, music only they can hear. Have you ever heard someone say, "And suddenly it seemed like we were the only two people in the room, the only two people in the world . . . " That's what sharing a sonnet in your lines is — sharing a special moment just between two people. As they are young and inexperienced, Romeo and Juliet jump into this romantic moment wholeheartedly, without hesitation. We have included for you both the party scene that was quoted above, and the famous "Balcony Scene," which is also filled with this special type of language.

It was Shakespeare who popularized the "we don't get along at all so we must be falling in love" characters. You've seen this in current movies many times; the movie *You've Got Mail* is a perfect example. We know going into the theater that this is a love story between Meg Ryan's character and Tom Hanks's character, and yet from the first time they meet, they fight like crazy. They secretly think, "He/she is really cute, but man, he/she totally gets on my nerves!" But by the end, they realize they've just misunderstood each other, and like all good romantic comedies, they make up in the end. One of Shakespeare's best love/hate couples is Beatrice and Benedick from *Much Ado About Nothing*. Sure, they fight from the moment they see each other:

BEATRICE
I wonder that you will still be talking, Signor Benedick,
no one marks you [is listening to you].
BENEDICK
Why, Lady Disdain! Are you yet living?

But their lines are just as unique as Romeo and Juliet's. This time, the lovers take each other's lines and twist them around to mock each other:

BEATRICE
A bird of my tongue is better than a beast of yours.
BENEDICK
I would my horse had the speed of your tongue. . .

Beatrice and Benedick are older than Romeo and Juliet (by today's standards, they would be in their late twenties or early thirties). They haven't been married before, but they have enough experience with love and heartbreak that they have both sworn off romance and marriage and struggle against their own feelings. We have included a short scene that shows off this love banter, and the scene where they finally admit their love to each other.

A twist on the traditional hate/love scene is found in Act 1, Scene 2 of *Richard III*. Most people wouldn't think of it as a love scene per se, because Richard only wants to marry Anne for her family title, and Anne despises Richard for good reason: He has killed her husband and her father-in-law. But though the scene starts with a knock-down, drag-out fight, and there is no real love between the characters, it does end with a marriage proposal, which Anne accepts. All through the scene, we see the same kind of word play that we saw in *Much Ado About Nothing*:

ANNE
   O, wonderful, when devils tell the truth!
RICHARD
   More wonderful when angels are so angry.

Why Anne accepts Richard's proposal is one of the great mysteries of Shakespeare, and each actress has to work out for herself how to get from point A ("I hate you") to point C ("I'll marry you"). One of the clues to that strange journey is in the structure of the language. She fights, he flirts. She curses, he compliments. This "love banter" structure catches her off-guard, throws her off-balance, and is the beginning of her losing her hold on logic and reason, which she mistakes for love. Anne at least has been married before, and she should know what love is. Though she accepts this strange proposal, she remains somewhat skeptical of Richard all the way through to the end of the scene.

One of the big questions for the actor is, "Does my character know that he or she is talking like this, in rhymes and poetry and word play?" The answer seems to be, yes. There are no hard and fast rules in acting, but think of it this way: When you're chatting someone up at a party or a dance ("Are your feet tired? Cuz you've been running through my mind all night . . ."), you know exactly what you're saying.

OK, that was a really cheesy line, but the principle is the same! You use lines that you know (or hope) will show the person that you are smart, funny, and charming, and you are carefully judging the effect they are having. Of course Juliet is thinking, "OK, I can rhyme with that," and Benedick (or Richard) is thinking, "I can turn that line around on her."

This is also another way that the characters are trying to apply logic to an illogical situation and maintain some control: "I will be clever and funny instead of just falling at her feet and begging her to love me, which is what I feel in my heart." (Or, in the case of Richard, "I will be clever by hiding my true intentions and tricking her into accepting me.")

JEALOUSY

If love is the nicest kind of madness, then jealousy is the sickest kind. Iago says in *Othello*, "Beware, my lord, of jealousy, for it is a green-eyed monster that doth mock the meat it feeds on." Jealousy is one of the main reasons why characters in Shakespeare plot and scheme and do horrible things to each other.

Before Shakespeare, there were two kinds of villains: the pure evil ones, which came from the character of the Devil in the morality plays, and villains motivated by jealousy in the revenge plays. As Shakespeare developed the modern villain — a complicated person with many motivations for committing evil acts — he started with jealousy as a motivation.

In the following short speeches, two men (in different plays) are looking at an innocent exchange between a man and a woman who are friends. In *Othello*, Iago is watching Othello's wife talking to a friend and sees that he can use this to make Othello jealous. Cassio is kissing Desdemona's hand by holding it up to his lips, but to be proper, he is actually pressing his lips to his own hand. Iago will use that properness to look like Cassio is covering up a lot worse.

IAGO

(Aside.) He takes her by the palm: ay, well said,

whisper: with as little a web as this will I
ensnare as great a fly as Cassio. Ay, smile upon
her, do; I will gyve thee in thine own courtship.
You say true; 'tis so, indeed: if such tricks as
these strip you out of your lieutenantry, it had
been better you had not kissed your three fingers so
oft, which now again you are most apt to play the
sir in. Very good; well kissed! an excellent
courtesy! 'tis so, indeed. Yet again your fingers
to your lips? would they were clyster-pipes for your sake!

In *The Winter's Tale*, Leontes watches his wife with their friend
and becomes convinced they are having an affair:

LEONTES
Too hot, too hot!
To mingle friendship far is mingling bloods.
I have a tremor cordis on me: my heart dances,
But not for joy, not joy. This entertainment
May a free face put on, derive a liberty
From heartiness, from bounty, fertile bosom,
And well become the agent, 't may, I grant;
But to be paddling palms and pinching fingers
As now they are, and making practiced smiles
As in a looking-glass, and then to sigh, as 'twere
The mort o'the deer; O, that is entertainment
My bosom likes not, nor my brows!

Note how in both situations, the people being talked about seem
to be doing just what Romeo and Juliet did in their first love scene —
holding hands and pressing palm to palm. This is another example
of how jealousy is love turned inside out.

One image to watch for when jealousy appears in the text is the
cuckold. A cuckold is a man who has been cheated on by his lover.
Legend has it that a cuckold grows horns from his head, which
shows everyone that he has been made a fool of. So you may hear

lines in Shakespeare like, "Is thicker than a cuckold's horn" or "God will send you no horns, Just, if he send me no husband." That's also why Leontes says his brows don't like what his wife is doing; he means he's going to grow horns on his forehead if she keeps it up.

The meter in jealousy scenes is often made up of people speaking over each other in a chaotic manner. Usually, it is the jealous person who has lines that are very broken up — short lines, shared lines, incomplete thoughts — while the other character who is being asked if they've noticed the deception or is being asked for advice has lines that are more calm and steady.

The first scene that we included is between Othello and Iago from *Othello*. Iago has been planting the idea in Othello's mind that Othello's wife, Desdemona, has been sleeping with their friend, Cassio. Iago is obviously trying to make Othello jealous, but there is an underlying message here too: Iago is doing this because he himself is jealous. He is jealous of Cassio, who got a promotion from Othello for a job Iago wanted, and he is jealous over his own wife, Emilia, because he thinks Othello slept with her.

Moreover, there is evidence in the text that Iago is jealous over the love that Desdemona and Othello have, since Iago is incapable of that kind of love (and has a terrible marriage with Emilia). Perhaps Iago is even secretly in love with Othello and is jealous because Othello loves Desdemona!

Whether you subscribe to these latter two ideas or not, it is clear from the play that Iago is torn up with jealousy, which means when he describes jealousy, he really knows what he's talking about.

In the second scene from *Othello*, Iago's trick is working, and Othello has become mad with jealousy. Iago once again goes to stoke the fires in Othello's heart. Notice how the language of this scene is somewhat similar to the love banter from the last section, as Iago invents innuendoes and hints at what he's trying to describe. This may be because jealousy is the flip side of love; or it may be because a jealous person can't stand to think about is going on but can't stop thinking about it either.

This is shown in the text as innuendo — "I have to talk about it, but I can't say it in plain terms." The best way to torture a jealous person? Give hints and let them imagine the rest, as in this quote from a later scene between Iago and Othello:

IAGO
> 'Faith, that [Cassio] did — I know not what he did.

OTHELLO
> What? What?

IAGO
> Lie —

OTHELLO
> With her?

IAGO
> With her, on her, what you will . . .

Returning to *The Winter's Tale*, in Act 1, Scene 2, Leontes, a king, has had a friend, Polixenes, visiting for several months — nine, to be exact, the same number of months that Leontes's wife, Hermione, has been pregnant. Polixenes has decided it is time for him to go back to his home. Leontes asks him to stay, but he will not. Leontes has his wife try to get him to stay — and it works.

Suddenly, Leontes is gripped with jealousy and becomes convinced that Polixenes and Hermione have been having an affair and that the baby that will be born any day is Polixenes's child. Leontes asks Camillo, his friend and servant, if he has noticed anything going on between Polixenes and Hermione. Leontes's lines are chaotic, while Camillo's are calm. It is easy to see Leontes's emotion and torment in this scene.

If you've ever been jealous of your girlfriend's ex-boyfriend or your boyfriend's other girlfriend, you will relate to Act 1, Scene 3 from *Antony and Cleopatra*. Antony is married but has left his wife in Rome and come to Egypt to negotiate with the Egyptian Queen, Cleopatra. They fall in love, and Antony stays in Egypt to have an affair with Cleopatra.

Antony has just received a letter from Rome that his wife has died, but Cleopatra is convinced that it is a letter from his wife calling him home. She is furious and feels betrayed. She attacks him, saying he never really loved her. When she finds out that his wife is dead, does that make her happy? No! She then attacks Antony saying if he can be happy to be free of his wife, then he will be equally happy when she, Cleopatra, herself is dead. Poor Antony can't win with a woman as jealous as that, he threatens to leave her entirely, which finally calms her down.

We see the same broken meter, shared lines, and short lines that we have seen in all these jealousy scenes. Added to this is poor Antony trying to get a word in, with entire lines consisting of "Cleopatra —," "Most sweet queen —," and "The gods best know —" (A word of caution: If you are flying-off-the-handle jealous or are dating someone who is and think you can use Shakespeare to justify your situation, remember that both Antony and Cleopatra end up dead by the end of the play.)

THE SUPERNATURAL

The supernatural and occult occasionally come into play in Shakespeare's dramas: fairies in *A Midsummer Night's Dream,* witches in *Macbeth,* the sorcerer Prospero in *The Tempest,* and ghosts returned from the dead in *Macbeth* and *Hamlet.*

In Shakespeare's day, and even later, fairies were considered to be another race that lived alongside humans, with their own kings and queens and religious rites, like dancing in the moonlight during a revel. (It's interesting to note that this could have been the description a Christian Britain would have used to describe the native Druid religion a thousand years before.)

Fairies were not necessarily nice creatures like Disney's Tinkerbell; they were magic creatures that had to be gotten along with, or they would wreak havoc in your home. Sure, if you leave out cookies and milk, the brownie fairies might come shine your shoes in the night, but if you made them angry, they could well steal your child to give to the fairy king or play terrible pranks on you.

There are several mentions in the plays of fairies "pinching" people. In *The Merry Wives of Windsor,* some of the characters pretend to be fairies in order to play a trick on Falstaff. We learn that fairies are known to be cruel ("Where fires thou find'st unraked and hearths unswept/There pinch the maids as blue as bilberry") and Falstaff even says, as if it is something everyone knows, "They are fairies; he that speaks to them shall die."

So it is really a marked change in Shakespeare's *A Midsummer Night's Dream* that the fairies are basically nice. Once again, Shakespeare is inventing something new, taking his audience's preconceptions and giving them something unexpected. These fairies do, in fact, play tricks on the lovers, making them all fall in love with the wrong people and giving Bottom the head of a donkey. They also play tricks on each other, like Oberon, the fairy king, making Titania, the fairy queen, fall in love with Bottom while he is magically transformed.

It is only Oberon's happiness at making up with Titania that spurs him to change everyone back to the way they were. In Act 3, Scene 1, Titania, under a spell, has fallen in love with Bottom and tells her fairies to attend on him. Since the fairies aren't usually nice to mortal people, this scene could be played against the lines, with the fairies unhappily helping Bottom. Keep this in mind: Fairies are supposed to be scary, not sweet and happy.

Equally frightening, in Shakespeare's day and ours, is the witch. It is no wonder that Shakespeare limited his use of witches. In his time many important people took witches very seriously, and several books were published describing witches and their powers as matters of scientific fact. The perception at the time was that witches were real and extremely dangerous, a threat to society and the civic order as well as to individuals.

Shakespeare's witches in *Macbeth* were derived from the legend of the Fates, characters in ancient Greek and Roman mythology. The Fates were three sisters (the witches in Macbeth are also called the Weird Sisters) who supposedly controlled human destiny (fate). One sister was concerned with the past, one with the future, and one with the present. Shakespeare mixed this concept with the idea of "real" witches and gave us some of our most enduring witch images, such as casting spells over a bubbling cauldron.

The Weird Sisters are oracles. They tell Macbeth of things to come and thus spur on the action of the play. They represent the supernatural world, the powers of the universe that know things but never tell us clearly what we should do. Unlike the fairies, they do not directly cause any action of the play. They tell Macbeth that he will be king, but do not say how; they tell him that he cannot be killed by a "man born of woman," but neglect to mention that there is one character in the play, Macduff, who was born by a cesarean section: He was taken out of his mother's belly by surgery and not born naturally through the birth canal.

The fairies and the witches share a more poetic language than the usual verse of the plays. While most of Shakespeare's plays are made up of iambic pentameter verse to create a heightened or more theatrical sense of reality, the fairies and witches are even more unreal than the human characters. The only way to show this in the language is to give them an even higher form of poetry, with a lot of rhyming and unique meter patterns. Look at this entrance line of Puck's in *A Midsummer Night's Dream:*

> Captain of our fairy band,
> Helena is here at hand;
> And the youth, mistook by me,
> Pleading for a lover's fee.
> Shall we their fond pageant see?
> Lord, what fools these mortals be!

Watch for this language shift and have fun with it!

There are several famous scenes about ghosts, mostly having to do with the dead crying out to have their deaths revenged. Death was a common occurrence in Shakespeare's time, with medical knowledge very limited and many people dying of the plague, childbirth, disease, and accident. Most people died in their homes with their families around them. Given the high mortality rate, someone who had managed to survive medieval life only to be murdered surely could not rest until his or her murder was avenged. Hamlet's father, for example, appears as a ghost and tells Hamlet to kill his uncle Claudius to avenge Old Hamlet's death.

Shakespeare was pretty careful (in an age where religious differences could get you thrown in jail) not to be too specific about ghosts and where they came from. Hamlet's father says, "I am forbid to tell the secrets of my prison house," meaning, he was allowed to come back but not to tell what the other side is like. We do, however, get the idea that he was in hell: "I could a tale unfold whose lightest word would harrow up thy soul, freeze thy young blood."

What does that tell us about the ghost of Hamlet's father? Was he not a good and honest person? If not, can Hamlet trust him? Another point brought up by a friend of Hamlet is that if the ghost came from hell, how do you know it's really Hamlet, Sr. and not the Devil in disguise? These ideas are not played out to the fullest in the text, however, as Hamlet quickly decides the Ghost was his father and was telling the truth.

Regardless, in Shakespeare, ghosts have only one emotion and one motivation: They cannot rest because they were murdered, and they are extremely angry about it and want the murderer to pay. It could be the murderer's own guilt that brings them back from the dead. They also have the ability to be invisible to all but the person whom they choose to see them, such as the Ghost of Banquo, who makes an appearance only to Macbeth at a crowded dinner table. It is sometimes argued that the Ghost of Banquo is a hallucination brought on by Macbeth's own guilt.

DISGUISE

Disguise and cross-dressing were conventions in several of Shakespeare's comedies. One of the best reasons for using this device so frequently was that boys played all the female roles! Women were not allowed to appear on the English stage at this time. Acting was considered to be an indecent profession for them, and one group, the Puritans, waged a full-bore attack on the theater and all forms of entertainment from dancing to card playing. Fortunately, the theater had a very strong supporter to offset the efforts of the Puritans. Queen Elizabeth was a great lover of theater and especially enjoyed Shakespeare's plays during the holiday season at court.

The characters of Portia, Rosalind, and Viola are often referred to as "trouser roles." This gender confusion must have been a great treat for the audience and a wonderful opportunity for Shakespeare to take advantage of any opportunity for innuendo. As Portia determines to follow after her new husband Bassanio, she says:

PORTIA
    Come on, Nerissa; I have work in hand
    That you yet know not of: we'll see our husbands
    Before they think of us.
NERISSA
    Shall they see us?
PORTIA
    They shall, Nerissa; but in such a habit,
    That they shall think we are accomplished
    With that we lack.
                    — *The Merchant of Venice*, Act 3, Scene 4

Disguise enables Portia to exercise her intelligence in a male arena, the courtroom, and to test Basanio by asking for her ring as payment for legal services. The audience can take delight in the device and enjoy the irony, knowing that before the comedy's end, all will be revealed.

Disguise plays a major role in Shakespeare's *Twelfth Night*. Some of the characters adopt deliberate disguises, such as Viola who is costumed as Cesario and Feste who plays the role of Sir Topas. Some characters are disguised (from others) through mistaken identity, such as when Antonio thinks Cesario is Sebastian and when Olivia believes Sebastian to be Cesario.

PLAYS WITHIN PLAYS

Three of Shakespeare's plays have plays inside them: *Hamlet, A Midsummer Night's Dream*, and *The Taming of the Shrew*. The plays themselves have different purposes (to trick the king into confessing in *Hamlet*, to entertain the duke in *A Midsummer Night's Dream*, to delude the drunk in *The Taming of the Shrew*), but each has a wealth of information about acting and the theater.

In *Hamlet*, a troupe of players (actors) has come to entertain the king with a play. Hamlet, who knows the actors from days gone by, intercepts them and asks that the players take a well-known play and change the story to a re-enactment of his father's murder, so that he can trap his uncle into confessing to the murder. A true performance is critical to Hamlet, as his plan will only work if the performance is realistic, understandable, and gripping.

After rewriting the play, he meets with the actors to give them a few pointers on acting. So it is our great fortune that we have acting lessons straight from William Shakespeare himself, in the form of a speech commonly known as "Hamlet's Speech to the Players." Since this is a set speech and not a dialogue scene, it is not included here, but it has a wealth of information about how Shakespeare wished his plays to be performed.

When Hamlet meets the players, he asks them if they know a play he'd seen and if they would perform a bit of it for them. After they leave, he marvels at the actor's ability to show emotion in a fake situation, when he himself can't express his real grief. When the players actually perform their play, which Hamlet calls *The Mousetrap*, Hamlet can hardly contain himself and ends up interrupting the performance with his own commentary.

In *A Midsummer Night's Dream*, we get a lot more information about how the plays were performed in Shakespeare's day, because we get to watch the actors (referred to in the play as "rude mechanicals," meaning they are laborers who do theater as a hobby) actually rehearse.

There was usually no director in Shakespeare's day; the actors directed themselves. Here, however, Peter Quince has clearly seen that if he doesn't take charge of the situation, nothing will get done. He chooses the play, hands out the parts, and directs the actors. He gives them each their own lines, not a copy of the whole play — which means no actor knows the entire play until it is finally performed.

He also says they must rehearse in the woods so that no one can spy on them and steal their ideas. This competitive aspect of theater was much more frequent in Shakespeare's day than it is now, when several productions of the same show might play in the same city. Quince might find this sort of ruthless, espionage-laced one-upmanship more common in today's film and television industries, where when one studio, sensing that another has a hit idea, tries to copy it and come out with the film first.

Hollywood also likes to take an old story and retell it, whether it is a modern version of a Shakespeare play or a remake of an old film. This is very similar to theater in the sixteenth century, where old familiar tales are turned into plays. Notice that when Quince announces the group will do the story of Pyramus and Thisbe, everyone already knows the story.

The difference between the plays-within-plays of *Hamlet* and *A Midsummer Night's Dream* is that the actors in *Hamlet* are talented professionals, whereas the "rude mechanicals" are untalented amateurs. Bottom fancies himself a great actor, but he has clearly never heard Hamlet's "Speech to the Players," for he blusters and overacts. He is better than his fellow actors only because they are awful. When the play is performed, they break character and speak to the audience, freeze up and panic, and mangle their lines.

In *The Taming of the Shrew*, the well-known story of Katharina and Petruchio's courtship and marriage is actually a play presented as a practical joke. *The Taming of the Shrew* begins with an Induction — a two-scene prologue in which a lord with a penchant for pranks discovers Christopher Sly, an itinerant tinker, dead drunk outside a country alehouse. The lord has Sly taken to his castle and put to sleep in the master bedroom; when Sly awakes, the lord and his companions convince the poor tinker that he is a nobleman who has been asleep for fifteen years. To celebrate his recovery, the lord brings in a group of players who then present a play, *The Taming of the Shrew*, which concludes five acts later without any further reference to Sly or the lord. The exact reason for this unresolved narrative framework is not entirely clear, but the deceptions played upon the tinker parallel the gross deceptions played in the main story on Katharina.

The challenge of the plays within plays is twofold. If you are playing one of the actors, you must deal with another form of heightened language. If the language of Hamlet is already heightened because it's a play, then the language in *The Mousetrap* must be more poetic to show that these characters are watching a play.

The language in Pyramus and Thisbe is even more strange, as the actors tend to get the extra-heightened lines wrong. If, on the other hand, you are playing a character who is watching the play, then you have your own challenge: You must watch the play intently so as not to draw the real audience's attention away from the miniplay, and you must react to what you are watching as your character would, laughing at the jokes, being shocked at the plot, and so on.

EPILOGUE

If you are looking for further advice on how best to approach a Shakespeare scene, why not go to the source?

Words without thoughts never to heaven go.

— *Hamlet*, Act 3, Scene 3

'Tis better to be brief than tedious.

— *Richard III*, Act 1, Scene 4

Wisely and slow; they stumble who run fast.

— *Romeo and Juliet*, Act 2, Scene 3

The silence often, of pure innocence persuades, when speaking fails.

— *Winter's Tale*, Act 2, Scene 2

Have patience, and endure.

— *Much Ado about Nothing*, Act 4, Scene 1

Courage and comfort, all shall yet go well.

— *King John*, Act 2, Scene 4

The sixty scenes in this collection offer a methodic skeleton key by which young actors may unlock a wide-ranging storehouse of inner emotion, which will help them embody more fully a particular character or moment.

In plain English, you can't beat a Shakespeare scene for a chance to tune up your acting chops. Use this book to expand your interpretive skills and discover new things about yourself as an actor — and person.

And always . . .

> To thine own self be true; and it must follow, as the night the day, thou can'st not then be false to any man.
>
> — *Hamlet*, Act 1, Scene 3

SCENES FOR
TWO CHARACTERS

ALL'S WELL THAT ENDS WELL

Act 4, Scene 2
2 Characters: 1 male, 1 female
Bertram (M), Diana (F)

Helena, who is trying to get her husband Bertram to declare his love for her, has promised Diana a large dowry if she can trick Bertram into giving up his priceless ring.

———⇒▷◦◁⇐———

Florence. The Widow's house. Enter BERTRAM and DIANA.

BERTRAM
They told me that your name was Fontibell.

DIANA
No, my good lord, Diana.

BERTRAM
Titled goddess;
And worth it, with addition! But, fair soul,
In your fine frame hath love no quality?
If quick fire of youth light not your mind,
You are no maiden, but a monument:
When you are dead, you should be such a one
As you are now, for you are cold and stem;
And now you should be as your mother was
When your sweet self was got.

DIANA
She then was honest.

BERTRAM
So should you be.

DIANA

No:
My mother did but duty; such, my lord,
As you owe to your wife.

BERTRAM

No more o' that;
I prithee, do not strive against my vows:
I was compell'd to her; but I love thee
By love's own sweet constraint, and will for ever
Do thee all rights of service.

DIANA

Ay, so you serve us
Till we serve you; but when you have our roses,
You barely leave our thorns to prick ourselves
And mock us with our bareness.

BERTRAM

How have I sworn!

DIANA

'Tis not the many oaths that makes the truth,
But the plain single vow that is vow'd true.
What is not holy, that we swear not by,
But take the High'st to witness: then, pray you, tell me,
If I should swear by God's great attributes,
I loved you dearly, would you believe my oaths,
When I did love you ill? This has no holding,
To swear by him whom I protest to love,
That I will work against him: therefore your oaths
Are words and poor conditions, but unseal'd,
At least in my opinion.

BERTRAM

Change it, change it;
Be not so holy-cruel: love is holy;
And my integrity ne'er knew the crafts
That you do charge men with. Stand no more off,

But give thyself unto my sick desires,
Who then recover: say thou art mine, and ever
My love as it begins shall so persever.

DIANA

I see that men make ropes in such a scarre
That we'll forsake ourselves. Give me that ring.

BERTRAM

I'll lend it thee, my dear; but have no power
To give it from me.

DIANA

Will you not, my lord?

BERTRAM

It is an honour 'longing to our house,
Bequeathed down from many ancestors;
Which were the greatest obloquy i' the world
In me to lose.

DIANA

Mine honour's such a ring:
My chastity's the jewel of our house,
Bequeathed down from many ancestors;
Which were the greatest obloquy i' the world
In me to lose: thus your own proper wisdom
Brings in the champion Honour on my part,
Against your vain assault.

BERTRAM

Here, take my ring:
My house, mine honour, yea, my life, be thine,
And I'll be bid by thee.

DIANA

    When midnight comes, knock at my chamber-window:
    I'll order take my mother shall not hear.
    Now will I charge you in the band of truth,
    When you have conquer'd my yet maiden bed,
    Remain there but an hour, nor speak to me:
    My reasons are most strong; and you shall know them
    When back again this ring shall be deliver'd:
    And on your finger in the night I'll put
    Another ring, that what in time proceeds
    May token to the future our past deeds.
    Adieu, till then; then, fail not. You have won
    A wife of me, though there my hope be done.

BERTRAM

    A heaven on earth I have won by wooing thee.

(Exit.)

DIANA

    For which live long to thank both heaven and me!
    You may so in the end.
    My mother told me just how he would woo,
    As if she sat in 's heart; she says all men
    Have the like oaths: he had sworn to marry me
    When his wife's dead; therefore I'll lie with him
    When I am buried. Since Frenchmen are so braid,
    Marry that will, I live and die a maid:
    Only in this disguise I think't no sin
    To cozen him that would unjustly win.

(Exit.)

ANTONY AND CLEOPATRA

Act 1, Scene 3
2 Characters: 1 male, 1 female
Mark Antony (M), Cleopatra (F)

Mark Antony tries to tell the news of his wife's death to his mistress, Cleopatra, who is so eaten up with jealousy that she won't let him speak.

⟶⊶⊷⟵

Alexandria. A room in Cleopatra's palace.

CLEOPATRA
I am sick and sullen.

MARK ANTONY
I am sorry to give breathing to my purpose, —

CLEOPATRA
Help me away, dear Charmian; I shall fall:
It cannot be thus long, the sides of nature
Will not sustain it.

MARK ANTONY
Now, my dearest queen, —

CLEOPATRA
Pray you, stand further from me.

MARK ANTONY
What's the matter?

CLEOPATRA
I know, by that same eye, there's some good news.
What says the married woman? You may go:
Would she had never given you leave to come!
Let her not say 'tis I that keep you here:

I have no power upon you; hers you are.

MARK ANTONY
The gods best know, —

CLEOPATRA
O, never was there queen
So mightily betray'd! yet at the first
I saw the treasons planted.

MARK ANTONY
Cleopatra, —

CLEOPATRA
Why should I think you can be mine and true,
Though you in swearing shake the throned gods,
Who have been false to Fulvia? Riotous madness,
To be entangled with those mouth-made vows,
Which break themselves in swearing!

MARK ANTONY
Most sweet queen, —

CLEOPATRA
Nay, pray you, seek no colour for your going,
But bid farewell, and go: when you sued staying,
Then was the time for words: no going then;
Eternity was in our lips and eyes,
Bliss in our brows' bent; none our parts so poor,
But was a race of heaven: they are so still,
Or thou, the greatest soldier of the world,
Art turn'd the greatest liar.

MARK ANTONY
How now, lady!

CLEOPATRA
I would I had thy inches; thou shouldst know
There were a heart in Egypt.

MARK ANTONY

Hear me, queen:
The strong necessity of time commands
Our services awhile; but my full heart
Remains in use with you. Our Italy
Shines o'er with civil swords: Sextus Pompeius
Makes his approaches to the port of Rome:
Equality of two domestic powers
Breed scrupulous faction: the hated, grown to strength,
Are newly grown to love: the condemn'd Pompey,
Rich in his father's honour, creeps apace,
Into the hearts of such as have not thrived
Upon the present state, whose numbers threaten;
And quietness, grown sick of rest, would purge
By any desperate change: my more particular,
And that which most with you should safe my going,
Is Fulvia's death.

CLEOPATRA

Though age from folly could not give me freedom,
It does from childishness: can Fulvia die?

MARK ANTONY

She's dead, my queen:
Look here, and at thy sovereign leisure read
The garboils she awaked; at the last, best:
See when and where she died.

CLEOPATRA

O most false love!
Where be the sacred vials thou shouldst fill
With sorrowful water? Now I see, I see,
In Fulvia's death, how mine received shall be.

MARK ANTONY

Quarrel no more, but be prepared to know
The purposes I bear; which are, or cease,
As you shall give the advice. By the fire

That quickens Nilus' slime, I go from hence
Thy soldier, servant; making peace or war
As thou affect'st.

CLEOPATRA

Cut my lace, Charmian, come;
But let it be: I am quickly ill, and well,
So Antony loves.

MARK ANTONY

My precious queen, forbear;
And give true evidence to his love, which stands
An honourable trial.

CLEOPATRA

So Fulvia told me.
I prithee, turn aside and weep for her,
Then bid adieu to me, and say the tears
Belong to Egypt: good now, play one scene
Of excellent dissembling; and let it look
Life perfect honour.

MARK ANTONY

You'll heat my blood: no more.

CLEOPATRA

You can do better yet; but this is meetly.

MARK ANTONY

Now, by my sword, —

CLEOPATRA

And target. Still he mends;
But this is not the best. Look, prithee, Charmian,
How this Herculean Roman does become
The carriage of his chafe.

MARK ANTONY

I'll leave you, lady.

CLEOPATRA

Courteous lord, one word.
Sir, you and I must part, but that's not it:
Sir, you and I have loved, but there's not it;
That you know well: something it is I would,
O, my oblivion is a very Antony,
And I am all forgotten.

MARK ANTONY

But that your royalty
Holds idleness your subject, I should take you
For idleness itself.

CLEOPATRA

'Tis sweating labour
To bear such idleness so near the heart
As Cleopatra this. But, sir, forgive me;
Since my becomings kill me, when they do not
Eye well to you: your honour calls you hence;
Therefore be deaf to my unpitied folly.
And all the gods go with you! upon your sword
Sit laurel victory! and smooth success
Be strew'd before your feet!

MARK ANTONY

Let us go. Come;
Our separation so abides, and flies,
That thou, residing here, go'st yet with me,
And I, hence fleeting, here remain with thee. Away!

(*Exeunt.*)

AS YOU LIKE IT

Act 3, Scene 2
2 Characters: 1 male, 1 female
Orlando (M), Rosalind (F)

The lovesick Orlando, pining for Rosalind, has been writing poems about her that he sticks on trees in the forest. Rosalind enters, disguised as a young man named Ganymede, and tells Orlando his lovesickness can be cured if he pretends that he (Ganymede) is Rosalind and comes to court him every day as if he were the real Rosalind. Orlando agrees, and they part.

———➤•◊•◄———

The forest.

ROSALIND
> *(Aside.)* I will speak to him, like a saucy lackey
> and under that habit play the knave with him.
> Do you hear, forester?

ORLANDO
> Very well: what would you?

ROSALIND
> I pray you, what is't o'clock?

ORLANDO
> You should ask me what time o' day: there's no clock
> in the forest.

ROSALIND
> Then there is no true lover in the forest; else
> sighing every minute and groaning every hour would
> detect the lazy foot of Time as well as a clock.

ORLANDO
> And why not the swift foot of Time? had not that
> been as proper?

ROSALIND

By no means, sir: Time travels in divers paces with
divers persons. I'll tell you who Time ambles
withal, who Time trots withal, who Time gallops
withal and who he stands still withal.

ORLANDO

I prithee, who doth he trot withal?

ROSALIND

Marry, he trots hard with a young maid between the
contract of her marriage and the day it is
solemnized: if the interim be but a se'nnight,
Time's pace is so hard that it seems the length of
seven year.

ORLANDO

Who ambles Time withal?

ROSALIND

With a priest that lacks Latin and a rich man that
hath not the gout, for the one sleeps easily because
he cannot study, and the other lives merrily because
he feels no pain, the one lacking the burden of lean
and wasteful learning, the other knowing no burden
of heavy tedious penury; these Time ambles withal.

ORLANDO

Who doth he gallop withal?

ROSALIND

With a thief to the gallows, for though he go as
softly as foot can fall, he thinks himself too soon there.

ORLANDO

Who stays it still withal?

ROSALIND

With lawyers in the vacation, for they sleep between
term and term and then they perceive not how Time moves.

ORLANDO

Where dwell you, pretty youth?

ROSALIND

With this shepherdess, my sister; here in the
skirts of the forest, like fringe upon a petticoat.

ORLANDO

Are you native of this place?

ROSALIND

As the cony that you see dwell where she is kindled.

ORLANDO

Your accent is something finer than you could
purchase in so removed a dwelling.

ROSALIND

I have been told so of many: but indeed an old
religious uncle of mine taught me to speak, who was
in his youth an inland man; one that knew courtship
too well, for there he fell in love. I have heard
him read many lectures against it, and I thank God
I am not a woman, to be touched with so many
giddy offences as he hath generally taxed their
whole sex withal.

ORLANDO

Can you remember any of the principal evils that he
laid to the charge of women?

ROSALIND

There were none principal; they were all like one
another as half-pence are, every one fault seeming
monstrous till his fellow fault came to match it.

ORLANDO

I prithee, recount some of them.

ROSALIND

No, I will not cast away my physic but on those that are sick. There is a man haunts the forest, that abuses our young plants with carving 'Rosalind' on their barks; hangs odes upon hawthorns and elegies on brambles, all, forsooth, deifying the name of Rosalind: if I could meet that fancy-monger I would give him some good counsel, for he seems to have the quotidian of love upon him.

ORLANDO

I am he that is so love-shaked: I pray you tell me your remedy.

ROSALIND

There is none of my uncle's marks upon you: he taught me how to know a man in love; in which cage of rushes I am sure you are not prisoner.

ORLANDO

What were his marks?

ROSALIND

A lean cheek, which you have not, a blue eye and sunken, which you have not, an unquestionable spirit, which you have not, a beard neglected, which you have not; but I pardon you for that, for simply your having in beard is a younger brother's revenue: then your hose should be ungartered, your bonnet unbanded, your sleeve unbuttoned, your shoe untied and every thing about you demonstrating a careless desolation; but you are no such man; you are rather point-device in your accoutrements as loving yourself than seeming the lover of any other.

ORLANDO

Fair youth, I would I could make thee believe I love.

ROSALIND

Me believe it! you may as soon make her that you
love believe it; which, I warrant, she is apter to
do than to confess she does: that is one of the
points in the which women still give the lie to
their consciences. But, in good sooth, are you he
that hangs the verses on the trees, wherein Rosalind
is so admired?

ORLANDO

I swear to thee, youth, by the white hand of
Rosalind, I am that he, that unfortunate he.

ROSALIND

But are you so much in love as your rhymes speak?

ORLANDO

Neither rhyme nor reason can express how much.

ROSALIND

Love is merely a madness, and, I tell you, deserves
as well a dark house and a whip as madmen do: and
the reason why they are not so punished and cured
is, that the lunacy is so ordinary that the whippers
are in love too. Yet I profess curing it by counsel.

ORLANDO

Did you ever cure any so?

ROSALIND

Yes, one, and in this manner. He was to imagine me
his love, his mistress; and I set him every day to
woo me: at which time would I, being but a moonish
youth, grieve, be effeminate, changeable, longing
and liking, proud, fantastical, apish, shallow,
inconstant, full of tears, full of smiles, for every
passion something and for no passion truly any
thing, as boys and women are for the most part

cattle of this colour; would now like him, now loathe him; then entertain him, then forswear him; now weep for him, then spit at him; that I drave my suitor from his mad humour of love to a living humour of madness; which was, to forswear the full stream of the world, and to live in a nook merely monastic. And thus I cured him; and this way will I take upon me to wash your liver as clean as a sound sheep's heart, that there shall not be one spot of love in't.

ORLANDO

I would not be cured, youth.

ROSALIND

I would cure you, if you would but call me Rosalind and come every day to my cote and woo me.

ORLANDO

Now, by the faith of my love, I will: tell me where it is.

ROSALIND

Go with me to it and I'll show it you and by the way you shall tell me where in the forest you live. Will you go?

ORLANDO

With all my heart, good youth.

ROSALIND

Nay you must call me Rosalind.

(Exeunt.)

HAMLET

Act 3, Scene 1
2 Characters: 1 male, 1 female
Hamlet (M), Ophelia (F)

Hamlet insults Ophelia and rejects her affection with a wild diatribe against women, leaving her to believe he is mad.

———➤◆◄———

A room in the castle.

OPHELIA
    Good my lord,
    How does your honour for this many a day?

HAMLET
    I humbly thank you; well, well, well.

OPHELIA
    My lord, I have remembrances of yours,
    That I have longed long to re-deliver;
    I pray you, now receive them.

HAMLET
    No, not I;
    I never gave you aught.

OPHELIA
    My honour'd lord, you know right well you did;
    And, with them, words of so sweet breath composed
    As made the things more rich: their perfume lost,
    Take these again; for to the noble mind
    Rich gifts wax poor when givers prove unkind.
    There, my lord.

HAMLET

Ha, ha! are you honest?

OPHELIA

My lord?

HAMLET

Are you fair?

OPHELIA

What means your lordship?

HAMLET

That if you be honest and fair, your honesty should admit no discourse to your beauty.

OPHELIA

Could beauty, my lord, have better commerce than with honesty?

HAMLET

Ay, truly; for the power of beauty will sooner transform honesty from what it is to a bawd than the force of honesty can translate beauty into his likeness: this was sometime a paradox, but now the time gives it proof. I did love you once.

OPHELIA

Indeed, my lord, you made me believe so.

HAMLET

You should not have believed me; for virtue cannot so inoculate our old stock but we shall relish of it: I loved you not.

OPHELIA

I was the more deceived.

HAMLET

Get thee to a nunnery: why wouldst thou be a
breeder of sinners? I am myself indifferent honest;
but yet I could accuse me of such things that it
were better my mother had not borne me: I am very
proud, revengeful, ambitious, with more offences at
my beck than I have thoughts to put them in,
imagination to give them shape, or time to act them
in. What should such fellows as I do crawling
between earth and heaven? We are arrant knaves,
all; believe none of us. Go thy ways to a nunnery.
Where's your father?

OPHELIA

At home, my lord.

HAMLET

Let the doors be shut upon him, that he may play the
fool no where but in's own house. Farewell.

OPHELIA

O, help him, you sweet heavens!

HAMLET

If thou dost marry, I'll give thee this plague for
thy dowry: be thou as chaste as ice, as pure as
snow, thou shalt not escape calumny. Get thee to a
nunnery, go: farewell. Or, if thou wilt needs
marry, marry a fool; for wise men know well enough
what monsters you make of them. To a nunnery, go,
and quickly too. Farewell.

OPHELIA

O heavenly powers, restore him!

HAMLET

I have heard of your paintings too, well enough; God

has given you one face, and you make yourselves
another: you jig, you amble, and you lisp, and
nick-name God's creatures, and make your wantonness
your ignorance. Go to, I'll no more on't; it hath
made me mad. I say, we will have no more marriages:
those that are married already, all but one, shall
live; the rest shall keep as they are. To a
nunnery, go.

(Exit.)

OPHELIA
O, what a noble mind is here o'erthrown!
The courtier's, soldier's, scholar's, eye, tongue, sword;
The expectancy and rose of the fair state,
The glass of fashion and the mould of form,
The observed of all observers, quite, quite down!
And I, of ladies most deject and wretched,
That suck'd the honey of his music vows,
Now see that noble and most sovereign reason,
Like sweet bells jangled, out of tune and harsh;
That unmatch'd form and feature of blown youth
Blasted with ecstasy: O, woe is me,
To have seen what I have seen, see what I see!

HENRY IV, PART I
Act 2, Scene 3
2 Characters: 1 male, 1 female
Hotspur (M), Lady Percy (F)

Lady Percy demands her husband, Hotspur, tell her about his up-coming military adventure. He playfully refuses, maintaining it is a military secret.

———➤•◀———

Warkworth castle.

LADY PERCY
But hear you, my lord.

HOTSPUR
What say'st thou, my lady?

LADY PERCY
What is it carries you away?

HOTSPUR
Why, my horse, my love, my horse.

LADY PERCY
Out, you mad-headed ape!
A weasel hath not such a deal of spleen
As you are toss'd with. In faith,
I'll know your business, Harry, that I will.
I fear my brother Mortimer doth stir
About his title, and hath sent for you
To line his enterprise: but if you go, —

HOTSPUR
So far afoot, I shall be weary, love.

LADY PERCY

>Come, come, you paraquito, answer me
>Directly unto this question that I ask:
>In faith, I'll break thy little finger, Harry,
>An if thou wilt not tell me all things true.

HOTSPUR

>Away,
>Away, you trifler! Love! I love thee not,
>I care not for thee, Kate: this is no world
>To play with mammets and to tilt with lips:
>We must have bloody noses and crack'd crowns,
>And pass them current too. God's me, my horse!
>What say'st thou, Kate? what would'st thou
>have with me?

LADY PERCY

>Do you not love me? do you not, indeed?
>Well, do not then; for since you love me not,
>I will not love myself. Do you not love me?
>Nay, tell me if you speak in jest or no.

HOTSPUR

>Come, wilt thou see me ride?
>And when I am on horseback, I will swear
>I love thee infinitely. But hark you, Kate;
>I must not have you henceforth question me
>Whither I go, nor reason whereabout:
>Whither I must, I must; and, to conclude,
>This evening must I leave you, gentle Kate.
>I know you wise, but yet no farther wise
>Than Harry Percy's wife: constant you are,
>But yet a woman: and for secrecy,
>No lady closer; for I well believe
>Thou wilt not utter what thou dost not know;
>And so far will I trust thee, gentle Kate.

LADY PERCY
> How! so far?

HOTSPUR
> Not an inch further. But hark you, Kate:
> Whither I go, thither shall you go too;
> To-day will I set forth, to-morrow you.
> Will this content you, Kate?

LADY PERCY
> It must of force.

> *(Exeunt.)*

MEASURE FOR MEASURE

Act 3, Scene 1
2 Characters: 1 male, 1 female
Claudio (M), Isabella (F)

Isabella tells ber brother Claudio that the only way he can be saved from execution is if she sleeps with Lord Angelo, who has imprisoned Claudio. Claudio encourages her to accept; Isabella angrily refuses.

⎯⎯⊷⊶⎯⎯

A room in the prison.

CLAUDIO
> Now, sister, what's the comfort?

ISABELLA
> Why,
> As all comforts are; most good, most good indeed.
> Lord Angelo, having affairs to heaven,
> Intends you for his swift ambassador,
> Where you shall be an everlasting leiger:
> Therefore your best appointment make with speed;
> To-morrow you set on.

CLAUDIO
> Is there no remedy?

ISABELLA
> None, but such remedy as, to save a head,
> To cleave a heart in twain.

CLAUDIO
> But is there any?

ISABELLA

> Yes, brother, you may live:
> There is a devilish mercy in the judge,
> If you'll implore it, that will free your life,
> But fetter you till death.

CLAUDIO

> Perpetual durance?

ISABELLA

> Ay, just; perpetual durance, a restraint,
> Though all the world's vastidity you had,
> To a determined scope.

CLAUDIO

> But in what nature?

ISABELLA

> In such a one as, you consenting to't,
> Would bark your honour from that trunk you bear,
> And leave you naked.

CLAUDIO

> Let me know the point.

ISABELLA

> O, I do fear thee, Claudio; and I quake,
> Lest thou a feverous life shouldst entertain,
> And six or seven winters more respect
> Than a perpetual honour. Darest thou die?
> The sense of death is most in apprehension;
> And the poor beetle, that we tread upon,
> In corporal sufferance finds a pang as great
> As when a giant dies.

CLAUDIO

> Why give you me this shame?

Think you I can a resolution fetch
From flowery tenderness? If I must die,
I will encounter darkness as a bride,
And hug it in mine arms.

ISABELLA

There spake my brother; there my father's grave
Did utter forth a voice. Yes, thou must die:
Thou art too noble to conserve a life
In base appliances. This outward-sainted deputy,
Whose settled visage and deliberate word
Nips youth i' the head and follies doth emmew
As falcon doth the fowl, is yet a devil
His filth within being cast, he would appear
A pond as deep as hell.

CLAUDIO

The prenzie Angelo!

ISABELLA

O, 'tis the cunning livery of hell,
The damned'st body to invest and cover
In prenzie guards! Dost thou think, Claudio?
If I would yield him my virginity,
Thou mightst be freed.

CLAUDIO

O heavens! it cannot be.

ISABELLA

Yes, he would give't thee, from this rank offence,
So to offend him still. This night's the time
That I should do what I abhor to name,
Or else thou diest to-morrow.

CLAUDIO

Thou shalt not do't.

ISABELLA

    O, were it but my life,
    I'ld throw it down for your deliverance
    As frankly as a pin.

CLAUDIO

    Thanks, dear Isabel.

ISABELLA

    Be ready, Claudio, for your death tomorrow.

CLAUDIO

    Yes. Has he affections in him,
    That thus can make him bite the law by the nose,
    When he would force it? Sure, it is no sin,
    Or of the deadly seven, it is the least.

ISABELLA

    Which is the least?

CLAUDIO

    If it were damnable, he being so wise,
    Why would he for the momentary trick
    Be perdurably fined? O Isabel!

ISABELLA

    What says my brother?

CLAUDIO

    Death is a fearful thing.

ISABELLA

    And shamed life a hateful.

CLAUDIO

    Ay, but to die, and go we know not where;

To lie in cold obstruction and to rot;
This sensible warm motion to become
A kneaded clod; and the delighted spirit
To bathe in fiery floods, or to reside
In thrilling region of thick-ribbed ice;
To be imprison'd in the viewless winds,
And blown with restless violence round about
The pendent world; or to be worse than worst
Of those that lawless and incertain thought
Imagine howling: 'tis too horrible!
The weariest and most loathed worldly life
That age, ache, penury and imprisonment
Can lay on nature is a paradise
To what we fear of death.

ISABELLA

Alas, alas!

CLAUDIO

Sweet sister, let me live:
What sin you do to save a brother's life,
Nature dispenses with the deed so far
That it becomes a virtue.

ISABELLA

O you beast!
O faithless coward! O dishonest wretch!
Wilt thou be made a man out of my vice?
Is't not a kind of incest, to take life
From thine own sister's shame? What should I think?
Heaven shield my mother play'd my father fair!
For such a warped slip of wilderness
Ne'er issued from his blood. Take my defiance!
Die, perish! Might but my bending down
Reprieve thee from thy fate, it should proceed:

I'll pray a thousand prayers for thy death,
No word to save thee.

CLAUDIO

Nay, hear me, Isabel.

ISABELLA

O, fie, fie, fie!
Thy sin's not accidental, but a trade.
Mercy to thee would prove itself a bawd:
'Tis best thou diest quickly.

CLAUDIO

O hear me, Isabella!

MUCH ADO ABOUT NOTHING

Act 1, Scene 1
2 Characters: 1 male, 1 female
Benedick (M), Beatrice (F)

Beatrice and Benedick haven't seen each other in a long time, but waste no time getting into a flirtatious confrontation.

———⊷•⊶———

Before Leonato's house.

BEATRICE

> I wonder that you will still be talking, Signior
> Benedick: nobody marks you.

BENEDICK

> What, my dear Lady Disdain! are you yet living?

BEATRICE

> Is it possible disdain should die while she hath
> such meet food to feed it as Signior Benedick?
> Courtesy itself must convert to disdain, if you come
> in her presence.

BENEDICK

> Then is courtesy a turncoat. But it is certain I
> am loved of all ladies, only you excepted: and I
> would I could find in my heart that I had not a hard
> heart; for, truly, I love none.

BEATRICE

> A dear happiness to women: they would else have
> been troubled with a pernicious suitor. I thank God

and my cold blood, I am of your humour for that: I
had rather hear my dog bark at a crow than a man
swear he loves me.

BENEDICK

God keep your ladyship still in that mind! so some
gentleman or other shall 'scape a predestinate
scratched face.

BEATRICE

Scratching could not make it worse, an 'twere such
a face as yours were.

BENEDICK

Well, you are a rare parrot-teacher.

BEATRICE

A bird of my tongue is better than a beast of yours.

BENEDICK

I would my horse had the speed of your tongue, and
so good a continuer. But keep your way, i' God's
name; I have done.

BEATRICE

You always end with a jade's trick: I know you of old.

MUCH ADO ABOUT NOTHING

Act 4, Scene 1
2 Characters: 1 male, 1 female
Benedick (M), Beatrice (F)

Beatrice and Benedick were in the process of secretly falling in love with each other when tragedy struck: Beatrice's cousin, Hero, was left at the altar by Benedick's best friend, Claudio, after Claudio told the whole church full of guests that Hero was sleeping around the night before their wedding. Hero is humiliated, and Beatrice is furious. Benedick tries to make her feel better by confessing his love for her, only to find that love put to the test by her bizarre demand that he kill Claudio.

———⟫•0•⟪———

A church.

BENEDICK
Lady Beatrice, have you wept all this while?

BEATRICE
Yea, and I will weep a while longer.

BENEDICK
I will not desire that.

BEATRICE
You have no reason; I do it freely.

BENEDICK
Surely I do believe your fair cousin is wronged.

BEATRICE
Ah, how much might the man deserve of me that would right her!

BENEDICK

Is there any way to show such friendship?

BEATRICE

A very even way, but no such friend.

BENEDICK

May a man do it?

BEATRICE

It is a man's office, but not yours.

BENEDICK

I do love nothing in the world so well as you: is
not that strange?

BEATRICE

As strange as the thing I know not. It were as
possible for me to say I loved nothing so well as
you: but believe me not; and yet I lie not; I
confess nothing, nor I deny nothing. I am sorry for my cousin.

BENEDICK

By my sword, Beatrice, thou lovest me.

BEATRICE

Do not swear, and eat it.

BENEDICK

I will swear by it that you love me; and I will make
him eat it that says I love not you.

BEATRICE

Will you not eat your word?

BENEDICK

With no sauce that can be devised to it. I protest
I love thee.

BEATRICE
Why, then, God forgive me!

BENEDICK
What offence, sweet Beatrice?

BEATRICE
You have stayed me in a happy hour: I was about to protest I loved you.

BENEDICK
And do it with all thy heart.

BEATRICE
I love you with so much of my heart that none is left to protest.

BENEDICK
Come, bid me do any thing for thee.

BEATRICE
Kill Claudio.

BENEDICK
Ha! not for the wide world.

BEATRICE
You kill me to deny it. Farewell.

BENEDICK
Tarry, sweet Beatrice.

BEATRICE
I am gone, though I am here: there is no love in you: nay, I pray you, let me go.

BENEDICK
> Beatrice, —

BEATRICE
> In faith, I will go.

BENEDICK
> We'll be friends first.

BEATRICE
> You dare easier be friends with me than fight with mine enemy.

BENEDICK
> Is Claudio thine enemy?

BEATRICE
> Is he not approved in the height a villain, that
> hath slandered, scorned, dishonoured my kinswoman? O
> that I were a man! What, bear her in hand until they
> come to take hands; and then, with public
> accusation, uncovered slander, unmitigated rancour,
> — O God, that I were a man! I would eat his heart
> in the market-place.

BENEDICK
> Hear me, Beatrice, —

BEATRICE
> Talk with a man out at a window! A proper saying!

BENEDICK
> Nay, but, Beatrice, —

BEATRICE
> Sweet Hero! She is wronged, she is slandered, she is undone.

BENEDICK

Beat —

BEATRICE

Princes and counties! Surely, a princely testimony,
a goodly count, Count Comfect; a sweet gallant,
surely! O that I were a man for his sake! or that I
had any friend would be a man for my sake! But
manhood is melted into courtesies, valour into
compliment, and men are only turned into tongue, and
trim ones too: he is now as valiant as Hercules
that only tells a lie and swears it. I cannot be a
man with wishing, therefore I will die a woman with grieving.

BENEDICK

Tarry, good Beatrice. By this hand, I love thee.

BEATRICE

Use it for my love some other way than swearing by it.

BENEDICK

Think you in your soul the Count Claudio hath wronged
Hero?

BEATRICE

Yea, as sure as I have a thought or a soul.

BENEDICK

Enough, I am engaged; I will challenge him. I will
kiss your hand, and so I leave you. By this hand,
Claudio shall render me a dear account. As you
hear of me, so think of me. Go, comfort your
cousin: I must say she is dead: and so, farewell.

(Exeunt.)

OTHELLO

Act 4, Scene 2
2 Characters: 1 male, 1 female
Othello (M), Desdemona (F)

Goaded to the breaking point by Iago's lies, Othello confronts Desdemona, his wife, and accuses her of unfaithfulness.

⟹●⟸

A room in the castle.

DESDEMONA
My lord, what is your will?

OTHELLO
Pray, chuck, come hither.

DESDEMONA
What is your pleasure?

OTHELLO
Let me see your eyes;
Look in my face.

DESDEMONA
What horrible fancy's this?
Upon my knees, what doth your speech import?
I understand a fury in your words.
But not the words.

OTHELLO
Why, what art thou?

DESDEMONA
Your wife, my lord; your true
And loyal wife.

OTHELLO

Come, swear it, damn thyself
Lest, being like one of heaven, the devils themselves
Should fear to seize thee: therefore be double damn'd:
Swear thou art honest.

DESDEMONA

Heaven doth truly know it.

OTHELLO

Heaven truly knows that thou art false as hell.

DESDEMONA

To whom, my lord? with whom? how am I false?

OTHELLO

O Desdemona! away! away! away!

DESDEMONA

Alas the heavy day! Why do you weep?
Am I the motive of these tears, my lord?
If haply you my father do suspect
An instrument of this your calling back,
Lay not your blame on me: If you have lost him,
Why, I have lost him too.

OTHELLO

Had it pleased heaven
To try me with affliction; had they rain'd
All kinds of sores and shames on my bare head.
Steep'd me in poverty to the very lips,
Given to captivity me and my utmost hopes,
I should have found in some place of my soul
A drop of patience: but, alas, to make me
A fixed figure for the time of scorn
To point his slow unmoving finger at!

Yet could I bear that too; well, very well:
But there, where I have garner'd up my heart,
Where either I must live, or bear no life;
The fountain from the which my current runs,
Or else dries up; to be discarded thence!
Or keep it as a cistern for foul toads
To knot and gender in! Turn thy complexion there,
Patience, thou young and rose-lipp'd cherubin, —
Ay, there, look grim as hell!

DESDEMONA

I hope my noble lord esteems me honest.

OTHELLO

O, ay; as summer flies are in the shambles,
That quicken even with blowing. O thou weed,
Who art so lovely fair and smell'st so sweet
That the sense aches at thee, would thou hadst
ne'er been born!

DESDEMONA

Alas, what ignorant sin have I committed?

OTHELLO

Was this fair paper, this most goodly book,
Made to write 'whore' upon? What committed!
Committed! O thou public commoner!
I should make very forges of my cheeks,
That would to cinders burn up modesty,
Did I but speak thy deeds. What committed!
Heaven stops the nose at it and the moon winks,
The bawdy wind that kisses all it meets
Is hush'd within the hollow mine of earth,
And will not hear it. What committed!
Impudent strumpet!

DESDEMONA

By heaven, you do me wrong.

OTHELLO

Are you not a strumpet?

DESDEMONA

No, as I am a Christian:
If to preserve this vessel for my lord
From any other foul unlawful touch
Be not to be a strumpet, I am none.

OTHELLO

What, not a whore?

DESDEMONA

No, as I shall be saved.

OTHELLO

Is't possible?

DESDEMONA

O, heaven forgive us!

OTHELLO

I cry you mercy, then:
I took you for that cunning whore of Venice
That married with Othello.

(Raising his voice.)

You, mistress,
That have the office opposite to Saint Peter,
And keep the gate of hell!

RICHARD III
Act 1, Scene 2
Characters: 1 male, 1 female
Gloucester (M), Lady Anne (F)

Hoping to win Lady Anne in marriage, Gloucester (Richard III's family name) surprises her as she grieves over the body of her father-in-law, who he has killed.

——➤◆◄——

Before the corpse of King Henry VI.

LADY ANNE
    What, do you tremble? are you all afraid?
    Alas, I blame you not; for you are mortal,
    And mortal eyes cannot endure the devil.
    Avaunt, thou dreadful minister of hell!
    Thou hadst but power over his mortal body,
    His soul thou canst not have; therefore be gone.

GLOUCESTER
    Sweet saint, for charity, be not so curst.

LADY ANNE
    Foul devil, for God's sake, hence, and trouble us not;
    For thou hast made the happy earth thy hell,
    Fill'd it with cursing cries and deep exclaims.
    If thou delight to view thy heinous deeds,
    Behold this pattern of thy butcheries.
    O, gentlemen, see, see! dead Henry's wounds
    Open their congeal'd mouths and bleed afresh!
    Blush, Blush, thou lump of foul deformity;
    For 'tis thy presence that exhales this blood
    From cold and empty veins, where no blood dwells;

Thy deed, inhuman and unnatural,
Provokes this deluge most unnatural.
O God, which this blood madest, revenge his death!
O earth, which this blood drink'st revenge his death!
Either heaven with lightning strike the
murderer dead,
Or earth, gape open wide and eat him quick,
As thou dost swallow up this good king's blood
Which his hell-govern'd arm hath butchered!

GLOUCESTER

Lady, you know no rules of charity,
Which renders good for bad, blessings for curses.

LADY ANNE

Villain, thou know'st no law of God nor man:
No beast so fierce but knows some touch of pity.

GLOUCESTER

But I know none, and therefore am no beast.

LADY ANNE

O wonderful, when devils tell the truth!

GLOUCESTER

More wonderful, when angels are so angry.
Vouchsafe, divine perfection of a woman,
Of these supposed-evils, to give me leave,
By circumstance, but to acquit myself.

LADY ANNE

Vouchsafe, defused infection of a man,
For these known evils, but to give me leave,
By circumstance, to curse thy cursed self.

GLOUCESTER

Fairer than tongue can name thee, let me have
Some patient leisure to excuse myself.

LADY ANNE

    Fouler than heart can think thee, thou canst make
    No excuse current, but to hang thyself.

GLOUCESTER

    By such despair, I should accuse myself.

LADY ANNE

    And, by despairing, shouldst thou stand excused;
    For doing worthy vengeance on thyself,
    Which didst unworthy slaughter upon others.

GLOUCESTER

    Say that I slew them not?

LADY ANNE

    Why, then they are not dead:
    But dead they are, and devilish slave, by thee.

GLOUCESTER

    I did not kill your husband.

LADY ANNE

    Why, then he is alive.

GLOUCESTER

    Nay, he is dead; and slain by Edward's hand.

LADY ANNE

    In thy foul throat thou liest: Queen Margaret saw
    Thy murderous falchion smoking in his blood;
    The which thou once didst bend against her breast,
    But that thy brothers beat aside the point.

GLOUCESTER

    I was provoked by her slanderous tongue,
    which laid their guilt upon my guiltless shoulders.

LADY ANNE

Thou wast provoked by thy bloody mind.
Which never dreamt on aught but butcheries:
Didst thou not kill this king?

GLOUCESTER

I grant ye.

LADY ANNE

Dost grant me, hedgehog? then, God grant me too
Thou mayst be damned for that wicked deed!
O, he was gentle, mild, and virtuous!

GLOUCESTER

The fitter for the King of heaven, that hath him.

LADY ANNE

He is in heaven, where thou shalt never come.

GLOUCESTER

Let him thank me, that holp to send him thither;
For he was fitter for that place than earth.

LADY ANNE

And thou unfit for any place but hell.

GLOUCESTER

Yes, one place else, if you will hear me name it.

LADY ANNE

Some dungeon.

GLOUCESTER

Your bed-chamber.

LADY ANNE

I'll rest betide the chamber where thou liest!

GLOUCESTER
    So will it, madam till I lie with you.

LADY ANNE
    I hope so.

GLOUCESTER
    I know so. But, gentle Lady Anne,
    To leave this keen encounter of our wits,
    And fall somewhat into a slower method,
    Is not the causer of the timeless deaths
    Of these Plantagenets, Henry and Edward,
    As blameful as the executioner?

LADY ANNE
    Thou art the cause, and most accursed effect.

GLOUCESTER
    Your beauty was the cause of that effect;
    Your beauty: which did haunt me in my sleep
    To undertake the death of all the world,
    So I might live one hour in your sweet bosom.

LADY ANNE
    If I thought that, I tell thee, homicide,
    These nails should rend that beauty from my cheeks.

GLOUCESTER
    These eyes could never endure sweet beauty's wreck;
    You should not blemish it, if I stood by:
    As all the world is cheered by the sun,
    So I by that; it is my day, my life.

LADY ANNE
    Black night o'ershade thy day, and death thy life!

GLOUCESTER
    Curse not thyself, fair creature thou art both.

LADY ANNE
    I would I were, to be revenged on thee.

GLOUCESTER
    It is a quarrel most unnatural,
    To be revenged on him that loveth you.

LADY ANNE
    It is a quarrel just and reasonable,
    To be revenged on him that slew my husband.

GLOUCESTER
    He that bereft thee, lady, of thy husband,
    Did it to help thee to a better husband.

LADY ANNE
    His better doth not breathe upon the earth.

GLOUCESTER
    He lives that loves thee better than he could.

LADY ANNE
    Name him.

GLOUCESTER
    Plantagenet.

LADY ANNE
    Why, that was he.

GLOUCESTER
    The selfsame name, but one of better nature.

LADY ANNE
    Where is he?

GLOUCESTER
    Here.

    (She spitteth at him.)

    Why dost thou spit at me?

LADY ANNE
    Would it were mortal poison, for thy sake!

GLOUCESTER
    Never came poison from so sweet a place.

LADY ANNE
    Never hung poison on a fouler toad.
    Out of my sight! thou dost infect my eyes.

GLOUCESTER
    Thine eyes, sweet lady, have infected mine.

LADY ANNE
    Would they were basilisks, to strike thee dead!

GLOUCESTER
    I would they were, that I might die at once;
    For now they kill me with a living death.
    Those eyes of thine from mine have drawn salt tears,
    Shamed their aspect with store of childish drops:
    These eyes that never shed remorseful tear,
    No, when my father York and Edward wept,
    To hear the piteous moan that Rutland made
    When black-faced Clifford shook his sword at him;
    Nor when thy warlike father, like a child,

Told the sad story of my father's death,
And twenty times made pause to sob and weep,
That all the standers-by had wet their cheeks
Like trees bedash'd with rain: in that sad time
My manly eyes did scorn an humble tear;
And what these sorrows could not thence exhale,
Thy beauty hath, and made them blind with weeping.
I never sued to friend nor enemy;
My tongue could never learn sweet smoothing word;
But now thy beauty is proposed my fee,
My proud heart sues, and prompts my tongue to speak.

(She looks scornfully at him.)

Teach not thy lips such scorn, for they were made
For kissing, lady, not for such contempt.
If thy revengeful heart cannot forgive,
Lo, here I lend thee this sharp-pointed sword;
Which if thou please to hide in this true bosom.
And let the soul forth that adoreth thee,
I lay it naked to the deadly stroke,
And humbly beg the death upon my knee.

(He lays his breast open: she offers at it with his sword.)

Nay, do not pause; for I did kill King Henry,
But 'twas thy beauty that provoked me.
Nay, now dispatch; 'twas I that stabb'd young Edward,
But 'twas thy heavenly face that set me on.

(Here she lets fall the sword.)

Take up the sword again, or take up me.

LADY ANNE
Arise, dissembler: though I wish thy death,
I will not be the executioner.

GLOUCESTER
    Then bid me kill myself, and I will do it.

LADY ANNE
    I have already.

GLOUCESTER
    Tush, that was in thy rage:
    Speak it again, and, even with the word,
    That hand, which, for thy love, did kill thy love,
    Shall, for thy love, kill a far truer love;
    To both their deaths thou shalt be accessary.

LADY ANNE
    I would I knew thy heart.

GLOUCESTER
    'Tis figured in my tongue.

LADY ANNE
    I fear me both are false.

GLOUCESTER
    Then never man was true.

LADY ANNE
    Well, well, put up your sword.

GLOUCESTER
    Say, then, my peace is made.

LADY ANNE
    That shall you know hereafter.

GLOUCESTER
    But shall I live in hope?

LADY ANNE
    All men, I hope, live so.

GLOUCESTER
    Vouchsafe to wear this ring.

LADY ANNE
    To take is not to give.

GLOUCESTER
    Look, how this ring encompasseth finger.
    Even so thy breast encloseth my poor heart;
    Wear both of them, for both of them are thine.
    And if thy poor devoted suppliant may
    But beg one favour at thy gracious hand,
    Thou dost confirm his happiness for ever.

LADY ANNE
    What is it?

GLOUCESTER
    That it would please thee leave these sad designs
    To him that hath more cause to be a mourner,
    And presently repair to Crosby Place;
    Where, after I have solemnly interr'd
    At Chertsey monastery this noble king,
    And wet his grave with my repentant tears,
    I will with all expedient duty see you:
    For divers unknown reasons. I beseech you,
    Grant me this boon.

LADY ANNE
    With all my heart; and much it joys me too,
    To see you are become so penitent.
    Tressel and Berkeley, go along with me.

GLOUCESTER
    Bid me farewell.

LADY ANNE
    'Tis more than you deserve;
    But since you teach me how to flatter you,
    Imagine I have said farewell already.

    (Exeunt LADY ANNE.)

ROMEO AND JULIET

Act 1, Scene 5
2 Characters: 1 male, 1 female
Romeo (M), Juliet (F)

Romeo sneaks into a party in the house of Juliet's family, where he speaks to her for the first time.

A hall in Capulet's house.

ROMEO

> If I profane with my unworthiest hand
> This holy shrine, the gentle fine is this:
> My lips, two blushing pilgrims, ready stand
> To smooth that rough touch with a tender kiss.

JULIET

> Good pilgrim, you do wrong your hand too much,
> Which mannerly devotion shows in this;
> For saints have hands that pilgrims' hands do touch,
> And palm to palm is holy palmers' kiss.

ROMEO

> Have not saints lips, and holy palmers too?

JULIET

> Ay, pilgrim, lips that they must use in prayer.

ROMEO

> O, then, dear saint, let lips do what hands do;
> They pray, grant thou, lest faith turn to despair.

JULIET

> Saints do not move, though grant for prayers' sake.

ROMEO

> Then move not, while my prayer's effect I take.
> Thus from my lips, by yours, my sin is purged.

(Kissing her.)

JULIET

> Then have my lips the sin that they have took.

ROMEO

> Sin from thy lips? O trespass sweetly urged!
> Give me my sin again.

JULIET

> You kiss by the book.

ROMEO AND JULIET

Act 2, Scene 2
2 Characters: 1 male, 1 female
Romeo (M), Juliet (F)

After the party where Romeo and Juliet have first spoken, Romeo has come into her garden and calls to her from underneath her bedroom window. They pledge their love to each other and agree to meet the next day.

⟫━◦━⟪

Capulet's orchard. Enter ROMEO.

ROMEO
　He jests at scars that never felt a wound.

(JULIET appears above at a window.)

　But, soft! what light through yonder window breaks?
　It is the east, and Juliet is the sun.
　Arise, fair sun, and kill the envious moon,
　Who is already sick and pale with grief,
　That thou her maid art far more fair than she:
　Be not her maid, since she is envious;
　Her vestal livery is but sick and green
　And none but fools do wear it; cast it off.
　It is my lady, O, it is my love!
　O, that she knew she were!
　She speaks yet she says nothing: what of that?
　Her eye discourses; I will answer it.
　I am too bold, 'tis not to me she speaks:
　Two of the fairest stars in all the heaven,
　Having some business, do entreat her eyes
　To twinkle in their spheres till they return.

What if her eyes were there, they in her head?
The brightness of her cheek would shame those stars,
As daylight doth a lamp; her eyes in heaven
Would through the airy region stream so bright
That birds would sing and think it were not night.
See, how she leans her cheek upon her hand!
O, that I were a glove upon that hand,
That I might touch that cheek!

JULIET

Ay me!

ROMEO

She speaks:
O, speak again, bright angel! for thou art
As glorious to this night, being o'er my head
As is a winged messenger of heaven
Unto the white-upturned wondering eyes
Of mortals that fall back to gaze on him
When he bestrides the lazy-pacing clouds
And sails upon the bosom of the air.

JULIET

O Romeo, Romeo! wherefore art thou Romeo?
Deny thy father and refuse thy name;
Or, if thou wilt not, be but sworn my love,
And I'll no longer be a Capulet.

ROMEO

(Aside.) Shall I hear more, or shall I speak at this?

JULIET

'Tis but thy name that is my enemy;
Thou art thyself, though not a Montague.
What's Montague? it is nor hand, nor foot,
Nor arm, nor face, nor any other part

Belonging to a man. O, be some other name!
What's in a name? that which we call a rose
By any other name would smell as sweet;
So Romeo would, were he not Romeo call'd,
Retain that dear perfection which he owes
Without that title. Romeo, doff thy name,
And for that name which is no part of thee
Take all myself.

ROMEO

I take thee at thy word:
Call me but love, and I'll be new baptized;
Henceforth I never will be Romeo.

JULIET

What man art thou that thus bescreen'd in night
So stumblest on my counsel?

ROMEO

By a name
I know not how to tell thee who I am:
My name, dear saint, is hateful to myself,
Because it is an enemy to thee;
Had I it written, I would tear the word.

JULIET

My ears have not yet drunk a hundred words
Of that tongue's utterance, yet I know the sound:
Art thou not Romeo and a Montague?

ROMEO

Neither, fair saint, if either thee dislike.

JULIET

How camest thou hither, tell me, and wherefore?
The orchard walls are high and hard to climb,

And the place death, considering who thou art,
If any of my kinsmen find thee here.

ROMEO

With love's light wings did I o'er-perch these walls;
For stony limits cannot hold love out,
And what love can do that dares love attempt;
Therefore thy kinsmen are no let to me.

JULIET

If they do see thee, they will murder thee.

ROMEO

Alack, there lies more peril in thine eye
Than twenty of their swords: look thou but sweet,
And I am proof against their enmity.

JULIET

I would not for the world they saw thee here.

ROMEO

I have night's cloak to hide me from their sight;
And but thou love me, let them find me here:
My life were better ended by their hate,
Than death prorogued, wanting of thy love.

JULIET

By whose direction found'st thou out this place?

ROMEO

By love, who first did prompt me to inquire;
He lent me counsel and I lent him eyes.
I am no pilot; yet, wert thou as far
As that vast shore wash'd with the farthest sea,
I would adventure for such merchandise.

JULIET

Thou know'st the mask of night is on my face,
Else would a maiden blush bepaint my cheek
For that which thou hast heard me speak to-night
Fain would I dwell on form, fain, fain deny
What I have spoke: but farewell compliment!
Dost thou love me? I know thou wilt say 'Ay,'
And I will take thy word: yet if thou swear'st,
Thou mayst prove false; at lovers' perjuries
Then say, Jove laughs. O gentle Romeo,
If thou dost love, pronounce it faithfully:
Or if thou think'st I am too quickly won,
I'll frown and be perverse an say thee nay,
So thou wilt woo; but else, not for the world.
In truth, fair Montague, I am too fond,
And therefore thou mayst think my 'havior light:
But trust me, gentleman, I'll prove more true
Than those that have more cunning to be strange.
I should have been more strange, I must confess,
But that thou overheard'st, ere I was ware,
My true love's passion: therefore pardon me,
And not impute this yielding to light love,
Which the dark night hath so discovered.

ROMEO

Lady, by yonder blessed moon I swear
That tips with silver all these fruit-tree tops —

JULIET

O, swear not by the moon, the inconstant moon,
That monthly changes in her circled orb,
Lest that thy love prove likewise variable.

ROMEO

What shall I swear by?

JULIET

Do not swear at all;
Or, if thou wilt, swear by thy gracious self,
Which is the god of my idolatry,
And I'll believe thee.

ROMEO

If my heart's dear love —

JULIET

Well, do not swear: although I joy in thee,
I have no joy of this contract to-night:
It is too rash, too unadvised, too sudden;
Too like the lightning, which doth cease to be
Ere one can say 'It lightens.' Sweet, good night!
This bud of love, by summer's ripening breath,
May prove a beauteous flower when next we meet.
Good night, good night! as sweet repose and rest
Come to thy heart as that within my breast!

ROMEO

O, wilt thou leave me so unsatisfied?

JULIET

What satisfaction canst thou have to-night?

ROMEO

The exchange of thy love's faithful vow for mine.

JULIET

I gave thee mine before thou didst request it:
And yet I would it were to give again.

ROMEO

Wouldst thou withdraw it? for what purpose, love?

JULIET

    But to be frank, and give it thee again.

    And yet I wish but for the thing I have:

    My bounty is as boundless as the sea,

    My love as deep; the more I give to thee,

    The more I have, for both are infinite.

    (Nurse calls within.)

    I hear some noise within; dear love, adieu!

    Anon, good nurse! Sweet Montague, be true.

    Stay but a little, I will come again.

    (Exit, above.)

ROMEO

    O blessed, blessed night! I am afeard.

    Being in night, all this is but a dream,

    Too flattering-sweet to be substantial.

    (Re-enter JULIET, above.)

JULIET

    Three words, dear Romeo, and good night indeed.

    If that thy bent of love be honourable,

    Thy purpose marriage, send me word to-morrow,

    By one that I'll procure to come to thee,

    Where and what time thou wilt perform the rite;

    And all my fortunes at thy foot I'll lay

    And follow thee my lord throughout the world.

    I come, anon. — But if thou mean'st not well,

    I do beseech thee —

    By and by, I come: —

    To cease thy suit, and leave me to my grief:

    To-morrow will I send.

ROMEO
    So thrive my soul —

JULIET
    A thousand times good night!

    (Exit, above.)

ROMEO
    A thousand times the worse, to want thy light.
    Love goes toward love, as schoolboys from
    their books,
    But love from love, toward school with heavy looks.

    (Retiring.)
    (Re-enter JULIET, above.)

JULIET
    Hist! Romeo, hist! O, for a falconer's voice,
    To lure this tassel-gentle back again!
    Bondage is hoarse, and may not speak aloud;
    Else would I tear the cave where Echo lies,
    And make her airy tongue more hoarse than mine,
    With repetition of my Romeo's name.

ROMEO
    It is my soul that calls upon my name:
    How silver-sweet sound lovers' tongues by night,
    Like softest music to attending ears!

JULIET
    Romeo!

ROMEO
    My dear?

JULIET

At what o'clock to-morrow
Shall I send to thee?

ROMEO

At the hour of nine.

JULIET

I will not fail: 'tis twenty years till then.
I have forgot why I did call thee back.

ROMEO

Let me stand here till thou remember it.

JULIET

I shall forget, to have thee still stand there,
Remembering how I love thy company.

ROMEO

And I'll still stay, to have thee still forget,
Forgetting any other home but this.

JULIET

'Tis almost morning; I would have thee gone:
And yet no further than a wanton's bird;
Who lets it hop a little from her hand,
Like a poor prisoner in his twisted gyves,
And with a silk thread plucks it back again,
So loving-jealous of his liberty.

ROMEO

I would I were thy bird.

JULIET

Sweet, so would I:
Yet I should kill thee with much cherishing.

Good night, good night! parting is such
sweet sorrow,
That I shall say good night till it be morrow.

(Exit above.)

ROMEO

Sleep dwell upon thine eyes, peace in thy breast!
Would I were sleep and peace, so sweet to rest!
Hence will I to my ghostly father's cell,
His help to crave, and my dear hap to tell.

(Exit.)

THE TAMING OF THE SHREW

Act 2, Scene 1
2 Characters: 1 male, 1 female
Petruchio (M), Katharina (F)

Petruchio and Katharina meet and immediately begin insulting each other. Petruchio vows he will marry her.

———◆———

A room in Baptista's house. Enter KATHARINA.

PETRUCHIO
>Good morrow, Kate; for that's your name, I hear.

KATHARINA
>Well have you heard, but something hard of hearing:
>They call me Katharina that do talk of me.

PETRUCHIO
>You lie, in faith; for you are call'd plain Kate,
>And bonny Kate and sometimes Kate the curst;
>But Kate, the prettiest Kate in Christendom
>Kate of Kate Hall, my super-dainty Kate,
>For dainties are all Kates, and therefore, Kate,
>Take this of me, Kate of my consolation;
>Hearing thy mildness praised in every town,
>Thy virtues spoke of, and thy beauty sounded,
>Yet not so deeply as to thee belongs,
>Myself am moved to woo thee for my wife.

KATHARINA
>Moved! in good time: let him that moved you hither
>Remove you hence: I knew you at the first
>You were a moveable.

PETRUCHIO
    Why, what's a moveable?

KATHARINA
    A join'd-stool.

PETRUCHIO
    Thou hast hit it: come, sit on me.

KATHARINA
    Asses are made to bear, and so are you.

PETRUCHIO
    Women are made to bear, and so are you.

KATHARINA
    No such jade as you, if me you mean.

PETRUCHIO
    Alas! good Kate, I will not burden thee;
    For, knowing thee to be but young and light —

KATHARINA
    Too light for such a swain as you to catch;
    And yet as heavy as my weight should be.

PETRUCHIO
    Should be! should — buzz!

KATHARINA
    Well ta'en, and like a buzzard.

PETRUCHIO
    O slow-wing'd turtle! shall a buzzard take thee?

KATHARINA
    Ay, for a turtle, as he takes a buzzard.

PETRUCHIO

Come, come, you wasp; i' faith, you are too angry.

KATHARINA

If I be waspish, best beware my sting.

PETRUCHIO

My remedy is then, to pluck it out.

KATHARINA

Ay, if the fool could find it where it lies,

PETRUCHIO

Who knows not where a wasp does
wear his sting? In his tail.

KATHARINA

In his tongue.

PETRUCHIO

Whose tongue?

KATHARINA

Yours, if you talk of tails: and so farewell.

PETRUCHIO

What, with my tongue in your tail? nay, come again,
Good Kate; I am a gentleman.

KATHARINA

That I'll try.

(She strikes him.)

PETRUCHIO

I swear I'll cuff you, if you strike again.

KATHARINA
So may you lose your arms:
If you strike me, you are no gentleman;
And if no gentleman, why then no arms.

PETRUCHIO
A herald, Kate? O, put me in thy books!

KATHARINA
What is your crest? a coxcomb?

PETRUCHIO
A combless cock, so Kate will be my hen.

KATHARINA
No cock of mine; you crow too like a craven.

PETRUCHIO
Nay, come, Kate, come; you must not look so sour.

KATHARINA
It is my fashion, when I see a crab.

PETRUCHIO
Why, here's no crab; and therefore look not sour.

KATHARINA
There is, there is.

PETRUCHIO
Then show it me.

KATHARINA
Had I a glass, I would.

PETRUCHIO
What, you mean my face?

KATHARINA

Well aim'd of such a young one.

PETRUCHIO

Now, by Saint George, I am too young for you.

KATHARINA

Yet you are wither'd.

PETRUCHIO

'Tis with cares.

KATHARINA

I care not.

PETRUCHIO

Nay, hear you, Kate: in sooth you scape not so.

KATHARINA

I chafe you, if I tarry: let me go.

PETRUCHIO

No, not a whit: I find you passing gentle.
'Twas told me you were rough and coy and sullen,
And now I find report a very liar;
For thou are pleasant, gamesome, passing courteous,
But slow in speech, yet sweet as spring-time flowers:
Thou canst not frown, thou canst not look askance,
Nor bite the lip, as angry wenches will,
Nor hast thou pleasure to be cross in talk,
But thou with mildness entertain'st thy wooers,
With gentle conference, soft and affable.
Why does the world report that Kate doth limp?
O slanderous world! Kate like the hazel-twig
Is straight and slender and as brown in hue
As hazel nuts and sweeter than the kernels.
O, let me see thee walk: thou dost not halt.

KATHARINA

    Go, fool, and whom thou keep'st command.

PETRUCHIO

    Did ever Dian so become a grove
    As Kate this chamber with her princely gait?
    O, be thou Dian, and let her be Kate;
    And then let Kate be chaste and Dian sportful!

KATHARINA

    Where did you study all this goodly speech?

PETRUCHIO

    It is extempore, from my mother-wit.

KATHARINA

    A witty mother! witless else her son.

PETRUCHIO

    Am I not wise?

KATHARINA

    Yes; keep you warm.

PETRUCHIO

    Marry, so I mean, sweet Katharina, in thy bed:
    And therefore, setting all this chat aside,
    Thus in plain terms: your father hath consented
    That you shall be my wife; your dowry 'greed on;
    And, Will you, nill you, I will marry you.
    Now, Kate, I am a husband for your turn;
    For, by this light, whereby I see thy beauty,
    Thy beauty, that doth make me like thee well,
    Thou must be married to no man but me;
    For I am he am born to tame you Kate,
    And bring you from a wild Kate to a Kate

Conformable as other household Kates.
Here comes your father: never make denial;
I must and will have Katharina to my wife.

THE WINTER'S TALE
Act 2, Scene 1
2 Characters: 1 male, 1 female
Leontes, Hermione

Obsessed by jealousy, Leontes, King of Sicilia, accuses Hermione, his wife, of adultery and declares her unborn child is that of Polixenes, King of Bohemia.

⇒►◆◄⇐

A room in Leontes's palace.

LEONTES
    I know't too well.
    Give me the boy: I am glad you did not nurse him:
    Though he does bear some signs of me, yet you
    Have too much blood in him.

HERMIONE
    What is this? sport?

LEONTES
    Bear the boy hence; he shall not come about her;
    Away with him! and let her sport herself
    With that she's big with; for 'tis Polixenes
    Has made thee swell thus.

HERMIONE
    But I'ld say he had not,
    And I'll be sworn you would believe my saying,
    Howe'er you lean to the nayward.

LEONTES
    You, my lords,

Look on her, mark her well; be but about
To say 'she is a goodly lady,' and
The justice of your hearts will thereto add
'Tis pity she's not honest, honourable:'
Praise her but for this her without-door form,
Which on my faith deserves high speech, and straight
The shrug, the hum or ha, these petty brands
That calumny doth use — O, I am out —
That mercy does, for calumny will sear
Virtue itself: these shrugs, these hums and ha's,
When you have said 'she's goodly,' come between
Ere you can say 'she's honest': but be 't known,
From him that has most cause to grieve it should be,
She's an adulteress.

HERMIONE
    Should a villain say so,
The most replenish'd villain in the world,
He were as much more villain: you, my lord,
Do but mistake.

LEONTES
    You have mistook, my lady,
Polixenes for Leontes: O thou thing!
Which I'll not call a creature of thy place,
Lest barbarism, making me the precedent,
Should a like language use to all degrees
And mannerly distinguishment leave out
Betwixt the prince and beggar: I have said
She's an adulteress; I have said with whom:
More, she's a traitor and Camillo is
A federary with her, and one that knows
What she should shame to know herself
But with her most vile principal, that she's
A bed-swerver, even as bad as those
That vulgars give bold'st titles, ay, and privy
To this their late escape.

HERMIONE

    No, by my life.
    Privy to none of this. How will this grieve you,
    When you shall come to clearer knowledge, that
    You thus have publish'd me! Gentle my lord,
    You scarce can right me throughly then to say
    You did mistake.

LEONTES

    No; if I mistake
    In those foundations which I build upon,
    The centre is not big enough to bear
    A school-boy's top. Away with her! to prison!
    He who shall speak for her is afar off guilty
    But that he speaks.

HERMIONE

    There's some ill planet reigns:
    I must be patient till the heavens look
    With an aspect more favourable. Good my lords,
    I am not prone to weeping, as our sex
    Commonly are; the want of which vain dew
    Perchance shall dry your pities: but I have
    That honourable grief lodged here which burns
    Worse than tears drown: beseech you all, my lords,
    With thoughts so qualified as your charities
    Shall best instruct you, measure me; and so
    The king's will be perform'd!

LEONTES

    Shall I be heard?

HERMIONE

    Who is't that goes with me? Beseech your highness,
    My women may be with me; for you see
    My plight requires it. Do not weep, good fools;

There is no cause: when you shall know your mistress
Has deserved prison, then abound in tears
As I come out: this action I now go on
Is for my better grace. Adieu, my lord:
I never wish'd to see you sorry; now
I trust I shall. My women, come; you have leave.

LEONTES
    Go, do our bidding; hence!

TROILUS AND CRESSIDA

Act 3, Scene 2
2 Characters: 1 male, 1 female
Troilus and Cressida

In the eighth year of the bloody Trojan War, the King of Troy's son, Troilus, is in love with the Trojan girl Cressida. Cressida's uncle, Pandarus, has arranged for Troilus and Cressida to meet, and they profess their love for each other.

———➤●◀———

Pandarus's orchard.

CRESSIDA
    Will you walk in, my lord?

TROILUS
    O Cressida, how often have I wished me thus!

CRESSIDA
    Wished, my lord! The gods grant, — O my lord!

TROILUS
    What should they grant? what makes this pretty
    abruption? What too curious dreg espies my sweet
    lady in the fountain of our love?

CRESSIDA
    More dregs than water, if my fears have eyes.

TROILUS
    Fears make devils of cherubims; they never see truly.

CRESSIDA

Blind fear, that seeing reason leads, finds safer
footing than blind reason stumbling without fear: to
fear the worst oft cures the worse.

TROILUS

O, let my lady apprehend no fear: in all Cupid's
pageant there is presented no monster.

CRESSIDA

Nor nothing monstrous neither?

TROILUS

Nothing, but our undertakings; when we vow to weep
seas, live in fire, eat rocks, tame tigers; thinking
it harder for our mistress to devise imposition
enough than for us to undergo any difficulty imposed.
This is the monstruosity in love, lady, that the will
is infinite and the execution confined, that the
desire is boundless and the act a slave to limit.

CRESSIDA

They say all lovers swear more performance than they
are able and yet reserve an ability that they never
perform, vowing more than the perfection of ten and
discharging less than the tenth part of one. They
that have the voice of lions and the act of hares,
are they not monsters?

TROILUS

Are there such? such are not we: praise us as we
are tasted, allow us as we prove; our head shall go
bare till merit crown it: no perfection in reversion
shall have a praise in present: we will not name
desert before his birth, and, being born, his addition

shall be humble. Few words to fair faith: Troilus
shall be such to Cressid as what envy can say worst
shall be a mock for his truth, and what truth can
speak truest not truer than Troilus.

TWELFTH NIGHT

Act 2, Scene 4
2 Characters: 1 male, 1 female
Duke Orsino (M), Viola (F)

Duke Orsino tells Viola (disguised as a boy, Cesario) to tell Countess Olivia of his love for her. Viola tells the Duke that Olivia does not love him, but he will not believe it and sends her off to the Countess.

Duke Orsino's palace.

DUKE ORSINO
>   Come hither, boy: if ever thou shalt love,
>   In the sweet pangs of it remember me;
>   For such as I am all true lovers are,
>   Unstaid and skittish in all motions else,
>   Save in the constant image of the creature
>   That is beloved. How dost thou like this tune?

VIOLA
>   It gives a very echo to the seat
>   Where Love is throned.

DUKE ORSINO
>   Thou dost speak masterly:
>   My life upon't, young though thou art, thine eye
>   Hath stay'd upon some favour that it loves:
>   Hath it not, boy?

VIOLA
>   A little, by your favour.

DUKE ORSINO
>   What kind of woman is't?

VIOLA

Of your complexion.

DUKE ORSINO

She is not worth thee, then. What years, i' faith?

VIOLA

About your years, my lord.

DUKE ORSINO

Too old by heaven: let still the woman take
An elder than herself: so wears she to him,
So sways she level in her husband's heart:
For, boy, however we do praise ourselves,
Our fancies are more giddy and unfirm,
More longing, wavering, sooner lost and worn,
Than women's are.

VIOLA

I think it well, my lord.

DUKE ORSINO

Then let thy love be younger than thyself,
Or thy affection cannot hold the bent;
For women are as roses, whose fair flower
Being once display'd, doth fall that very hour.

VIOLA

And so they are: alas, that they are so;
To die, even when they to perfection grow!

DUKE ORSINO

Once more, Cesario,
Get thee to yond same sovereign cruelty:
Tell her, my love, more noble than the world,
Prizes not quantity of dirty lands;

The parts that fortune hath bestow'd upon her,
Tell her, I hold as giddily as fortune;
But 'tis that miracle and queen of gems
That nature pranks her in attracts my soul.

VIOLA
But if she cannot love you, sir?

DUKE ORSINO
I cannot be so answer'd.

VIOLA
Sooth, but you must.
Say that some lady, as perhaps there is,
Hath for your love a great a pang of heart
As you have for Olivia: you cannot love her;
You tell her so; must she not then be answer'd?

DUKE ORSINO
There is no woman's sides
Can bide the beating of so strong a passion
As love doth give my heart; no woman's heart
So big, to hold so much; they lack retention
Alas, their love may be call'd appetite,
No motion of the liver, but the palate,
That suffer surfeit, cloyment and revolt;
But mine is all as hungry as the sea,
And can digest as much: make no compare
Between that love a woman can bear me
And that I owe Olivia.

VIOLA
Ay, but I know —

DUKE ORSINO
What dost thou know?

VIOLA

Too well what love women to men may owe:
In faith, they are as true of heart as we.
My father had a daughter loved a man,
As it might be, perhaps, were I a woman,
I should your lordship.

DUKE ORSINO

And what's her history?

VIOLA

A blank, my lord. She never told her love,
But let concealment, like a worm i' the bud,
Feed on her damask cheek: she pined in thought,
And with a green and yellow melancholy
She sat like patience on a monument,
Smiling at grief. Was not this love indeed?
We men may say more, swear more: but indeed
Our shows are more than will; for still we prove
Much in our vows, but little in our love.

DUKE ORSINO

But died thy sister of her love, my boy?

VIOLA

I am all the daughters of my father's house,
And all the brothers too: and yet I know not.
Sir, shall I to this lady?

DUKE ORSINO

Ay, that's the theme.
To her in haste; give her this jewel; say,
My love can give no place, bide no denay.

(Exeunt.)

HAMLET

Act 1, Scene 5
2 Characters: 2 male
Hamlet, Hamlet's father's ghost

The Ghost of Hamlet's father, killed recently by persons at this point unknown, has been seen wandering the castle. Hamlet waits for him and confronts him to find out what he wants.

———➤•◦•◄———

Elsinore. A platform before the castle. Enter GHOST and HAMLET.

HAMLET
Where wilt thou lead me? speak; I'll go no further.

GHOST
Mark me.

HAMLET
I will.

GHOST
My hour is almost come,
When I to sulphurous and tormenting flames
Must render up myself.

HAMLET
Alas, poor ghost!

GHOST
Pity me not, but lend thy serious hearing
To what I shall unfold.

HAMLET

Speak; I am bound to hear.

GHOST

So art thou to revenge, when thou shalt hear.

HAMLET

What?

GHOST

I am thy father's spirit,
Doom'd for a certain term to walk the night,
And for the day confined to fast in fires,
Till the foul crimes done in my days of nature
Are burnt and purged away. But that I am forbid
To tell the secrets of my prison-house,
I could a tale unfold whose lightest word
Would harrow up thy soul, freeze thy young blood,
Make thy two eyes, like stars, start from their spheres,
Thy knotted and combined locks to part
And each particular hair to stand on end,
Like quills upon the fretful porpentine:
But this eternal blazon must not be
To ears of flesh and blood. List, list, O, list!
If thou didst ever thy dear father love —

HAMLET

O God!

GHOST

Revenge his foul and most unnatural murder.

HAMLET

Murder!

GHOST

Murder most foul, as in the best it is;
But this most foul, strange and unnatural.

HAMLET

    Haste me to know't, that I, with wings as swift

    As meditation or the thoughts of love,

    May sweep to my revenge.

GHOST

    I find thee apt;

    And duller shouldst thou be than the fat weed

    That roots itself in ease on Lethe wharf,

    Wouldst thou not stir in this. Now, Hamlet, hear:

    'Tis given out that, sleeping in my orchard,

    A serpent stung me; so the whole ear of Denmark

    Is by a forged process of my death

    Rankly abused: but know, thou noble youth,

    The serpent that did sting thy father's life

    Now wears his crown.

HAMLET

    O my prophetic soul! My uncle!

GHOST

    Ay, that incestuous, that adulterate beast,

    With witchcraft of his wit, with traitorous gifts, —

    O wicked wit and gifts, that have the power

    So to seduce! — won to his shameful lust

    The will of my most seeming-virtuous queen:

    O Hamlet, what a falling-off was there!

    From me, whose love was of that dignity

    That it went hand in hand even with the vow

    I made to her in marriage, and to decline

    Upon a wretch whose natural gifts were poor

    To those of mine!

    But virtue, as it never will be moved,

    Though lewdness court it in a shape of heaven,

    So lust, though to a radiant angel link'd,

    Will sate itself in a celestial bed,

And prey on garbage.
But, soft! methinks I scent the morning air;
Brief let me be. Sleeping within my orchard,
My custom always of the afternoon,
Upon my secure hour thy uncle stole,
With juice of cursed hebenon in a vial,
And in the porches of my ears did pour
The leperous distilment; whose effect
Holds such an enmity with blood of man
That swift as quicksilver it courses through
The natural gates and alleys of the body,
And with a sudden vigour doth posset
And curd, like eager droppings into milk,
The thin and wholesome blood: so did it mine;
And a most instant tetter bark'd about,
Most lazar-like, with vile and loathsome crust,
All my smooth body.
Thus was I, sleeping, by a brother's hand
Of life, of crown, of queen, at once dispatch'd:
Cut off even in the blossoms of my sin,
Unhousel'd, disappointed, unanel'd,
No reckoning made, but sent to my account
With all my imperfections on my head:
O, horrible! O, horrible! most horrible!
If thou hast nature in thee, bear it not;
Let not the royal bed of Denmark be
A couch for luxury and damned incest.
But, howsoever thou pursuest this act,
Taint not thy mind, nor let thy soul contrive
Against thy mother aught: leave her to heaven
And to those thorns that in her bosom lodge,
To prick and sting her. Fare thee well at once!
The glow-worm shows the matin to be near,
And 'gins to pale his uneffectual fire:
Adieu, adieu! Hamlet, remember me.

(Exit.)

HAMLET
    O all you host of heaven! O earth! what else?
    And shall I couple hell? O, fie! Hold, hold, my heart;
    And you, my sinews, grow not instant old,
    But bear me stiffly up. Remember thee!
    Ay, thou poor ghost, while memory holds a seat
    In this distracted globe. Remember thee!
    Yea, from the table of my memory
    I'll wipe away all trivial fond records,
    All saws of books, all forms, all pressures past,
    That youth and observation copied there;
    And thy commandment all alone shall live
    Within the book and volume of my brain,
    Unmix'd with baser matter: yes, by heaven!
    O most pernicious woman!
    O villain, villain, smiling, damned villain!
    My tables, — meet it is I set it down,
    That one may smile, and smile, and be a villain;
    At least I'm sure it may be so in Denmark:

(Writing.)

    So, uncle, there you are. Now to my word;
    It is 'Adieu, adieu! remember me.'
    I have sworn 't.

OTHELLO
Act 3, Scene 3
Characters: 2 male
Othello, Iago

Iago plants the seeds of suspicion in the mind of Othello that Othello's wife, Desdemona, has been having an affair with Cassio.

———➤●◀———

The garden of the castle. Exeunt DESDEMONA and EMILIA.

OTHELLO
> Excellent wretch! Perdition catch my soul,
> But I do love thee! and when I love thee not,
> Chaos is come again.

IAGO
> My noble lord —

OTHELLO
> What dost thou say, Iago?

IAGO
> Did Michael Cassio, when you woo'd my lady,
> Know of your love?

OTHELLO
> He did, from first to last: why dost thou ask?

IAGO
> But for a satisfaction of my thought;
> No further harm.

OTHELLO
> Why of thy thought, Iago?

IAGO

    I did not think he had been acquainted with her.

OTHELLO

    O, yes; and went between us very oft.

IAGO

    Indeed!

OTHELLO

    Indeed! ay, indeed: discern'st thou aught in that?
    Is he not honest?

IAGO

    Honest, my lord!

OTHELLO

    Honest! ay, honest.

IAGO

    My lord, for aught I know.

OTHELLO

    What dost thou think?

IAGO

    Think, my lord!

OTHELLO

    Think, my lord!
    By heaven, he echoes me,
    As if there were some monster in his thought
    Too hideous to be shown. Thou dost mean something:
    I heard thee say even now, thou likedst not that,
    When Cassio left my wife: what didst not like?
    And when I told thee he was of my counsel

In my whole course of wooing, thou criedst 'Indeed!'
And didst contract and purse thy brow together,
As if thou then hadst shut up in thy brain
Some horrible conceit: if thou dost love me,
Show me thy thought.

IAGO

My lord, you know I love you.

OTHELLO

I think thou dost;
And, for I know thou'rt full of love and honesty,
And weigh'st thy words before thou givest them breath,
Therefore these stops of thine fright me the more:
For such things in a false disloyal knave
Are tricks of custom, but in a man that's just
They are close delations, working from the heart
That passion cannot rule.

IAGO

For Michael Cassio,
I dare be sworn I think that he is honest.

OTHELLO

I think so too.

IAGO

Men should be what they seem;
Or those that be not, would they might seem none!

OTHELLO

Certain, men should be what they seem.

IAGO

Why, then, I think Cassio's an honest man.

OTHELLO

    Nay, yet there's more in this:
    I prithee, speak to me as to thy thinkings,
    As thou dost ruminate, and give thy worst of thoughts
    The worst of words.

IAGO

    Good my lord, pardon me:
    Though I am bound to every act of duty,
    I am not bound to that all slaves are free to.
    Utter my thoughts? Why, say they are vile and false;
    As where's that palace whereinto foul things
    Sometimes intrude not? who has a breast so pure,
    But some uncleanly apprehensions
    Keep leets and law-days and in session sit
    With meditations lawful?

OTHELLO

    Thou dost conspire against thy friend, Iago,
    If thou but think'st him wrong'd and makest his ear
    A stranger to thy thoughts.

IAGO

    I do beseech you —
    Though I perchance am vicious in my guess,
    As, I confess, it is my nature's plague
    To spy into abuses, and oft my jealousy
    Shapes faults that are not — that your wisdom yet,
    From one that so imperfectly conceits,
    Would take no notice, nor build yourself a trouble
    Out of his scattering and unsure observance.
    It were not for your quiet nor your good,
    Nor for my manhood, honesty, or wisdom,
    To let you know my thoughts.

OTHELLO

    What dost thou mean?

IAGO

    Good name in man and woman, dear my lord,
    Is the immediate jewel of their souls:
    Who steals my purse steals trash; 'tis something, nothing;
    'Twas mine, 'tis his, and has been slave to thousands:
    But he that filches from me my good name
    Robs me of that which not enriches him
    And makes me poor indeed.

OTHELLO

    By heaven, I'll know thy thoughts.

IAGO

    You cannot, if my heart were in your hand;
    Nor shall not, whilst 'tis in my custody.

OTHELLO

    Ha!

IAGO

    O, beware, my lord, of jealousy;
    It is the green-eyed monster which doth mock
    The meat it feeds on; that cuckold lives in bliss
    Who, certain of his fate, loves not his wronger;
    But, O, what damned minutes tells he o'er
    Who dotes, yet doubts, suspects, yet strongly loves!

OTHELLO

    O misery!

IAGO

    Poor and content is rich and rich enough,
    But riches fineless is as poor as winter

To him that ever fears he shall be poor.
Good heaven, the souls of all my tribe defend
From jealousy!

OTHELLO

Why, why is this?
Think'st thou I'ld make a lie of jealousy,
To follow still the changes of the moon
With fresh suspicions? No; to be once in doubt
Is once to be resolved: exchange me for a goat,
When I shall turn the business of my soul
To such exsufflicate and blown surmises,
Matching thy inference. 'Tis not to make me jealous
To say my wife is fair, feeds well, loves company,
Is free of speech, sings, plays and dances well;
Where virtue is, these are more virtuous:
Nor from mine own weak merits will I draw
The smallest fear or doubt of her revolt;
For she had eyes, and chose me. No, Iago;
I'll see before I doubt; when I doubt, prove;
And on the proof, there is no more but this, —
Away at once with love or jealousy!

IAGO

I am glad of it; for now I shall have reason
To show the love and duty that I bear you
With franker spirit: therefore, as I am bound,
Receive it from me. I speak not yet of proof.
Look to your wife; observe her well with Cassio;
Wear your eye thus, not jealous nor secure:
I would not have your free and noble nature,
Out of self-bounty, be abused; look to't:
I know our country disposition well;
In Venice they do let heaven see the pranks
They dare not show their husbands; their best conscience
Is not to leave't undone, but keep't unknown.

OTHELLO

Dost thou say so?

IAGO

She did deceive her father, marrying you;
And when she seem'd to shake and fear your looks,
She loved them most.

OTHELLO

And so she did.

IAGO

Why, go to then;
She that, so young, could give out such a seeming,
To seal her father's eyes up close as oak —
He thought 'twas witchcraft — but I am much to blame;
I humbly do beseech you of your pardon
For too much loving you.

OTHELLO

I am bound to thee for ever.

IAGO

I see this hath a little dash'd your spirits.

OTHELLO

Not a jot, not a jot.

IAGO

I' faith, I fear it has.
I hope you will consider what is spoke
Comes from my love. But I do see you're moved:
I am to pray you not to strain my speech
To grosser issues nor to larger reach
Than to suspicion.

OTHELLO

I will not.

IAGO

Should you do so, my lord,
My speech should fall into such vile success
As my thoughts aim not at. Cassio's my worthy friend —
My lord, I see you're moved.

OTHELLO

No, not much moved:
I do not think but Desdemona's honest.

IAGO

Long live she so! and long live you to think so!

OTHELLO

And yet, how nature erring from itself, —

IAGO

Ay, there's the point: as — to be bold with you —
Not to affect many proposed matches
Of her own clime, complexion, and degree,
Whereto we see in all things nature tends —
Foh! one may smell in such a will most rank,
Foul disproportion thoughts unnatural.
But pardon me; I do not in position
Distinctly speak of her; though I may fear
Her will, recoiling to her better judgment,
May fall to match you with her country forms
And happily repent.

OTHELLO

Farewell, farewell:
If more thou dost perceive, let me know more;
Set on thy wife to observe: leave me, Iago:

IAGO

(Going.) My lord, I take my leave.

OTHELLO

Why did I marry? This honest creature doubtless
Sees and knows more, much more, than he unfolds.

IAGO

(Returning.) My lord, I would I might entreat
your honour
To scan this thing no further; leave it to time:
Though it be fit that Cassio have his place,
For sure, he fills it up with great ability,
Yet, if you please to hold him off awhile,
You shall by that perceive him and his means:
Note, if your lady strain his entertainment
With any strong or vehement importunity;
Much will be seen in that. In the mean time,
Let me be thought too busy in my fears —
As worthy cause I have to fear I am —
And hold her free, I do beseech your honour.

OTHELLO

Fear not my government.

IAGO

I once more take my leave.

(Exit.)

OTHELLO

This fellow's of exceeding honesty,
And knows all qualities, with a learned spirit,
Of human dealings. If I do prove her haggard,
Though that her jesses were my dear heartstrings,
I'ld whistle her off and let her down the wind,

To pray at fortune. Haply, for I am black
And have not those soft parts of conversation
That chamberers have, or for I am declined
Into the vale of years, — yet that's not much —
She's gone. I am abused; and my relief
Must be to loathe her. O curse of marriage,
That we can call these delicate creatures ours,
And not their appetites! I had rather be a toad,
And live upon the vapour of a dungeon,
Than keep a corner in the thing I love
For others' uses. Yet, 'tis the plague of great ones;
Prerogatived are they less than the base;
'Tis destiny unshunnable, like death:
Even then this forked plague is fated to us
When we do quicken. Desdemona comes:
If she be false, O, then heaven mocks itself!
I'll not believe't.

OTHELLO
Act 4, Scene 1
Characters: 2 male
Othello, Iago

Iago continues to feed Othello lies about Cassio and Desdemona;
Othello is becoming convinced that Iago is right and the affair is real.

———➤●◀———

Cyprus. Before the castle. Enter OTHELLO and IAGO.

IAGO
Will you think so?

OTHELLO
Think so, Iago!

IAGO
What,
To kiss in private?

OTHELLO
An unauthorized kiss.

IAGO
Or to be naked with her friend in bed
An hour or more, not meaning any harm?

OTHELLO
Naked in bed, Iago, and not mean harm!
It is hypocrisy against the devil:
They that mean virtuously, and yet do so,
The devil their virtue tempts, and they tempt heaven.

IAGO
So they do nothing, 'tis a venial slip:
But if I give my wife a handkerchief, —

OTHELLO
What then?

IAGO

> Why, then, 'tis hers, my lord; and, being hers,
> She may, I think, bestow't on any man.

OTHELLO

> She is protectress of her honour too:
> May she give that?

IAGO

> Her honour is an essence that's not seen;
> They have it very oft that have it not:
> But, for the handkerchief, —

OTHELLO

> By heaven, I would most gladly have forgot it.
> Thou said'st, it comes o'er my memory,
> As doth the raven o'er the infected house,
> Boding to all — he had my handkerchief.

IAGO

> Ay, what of that?

OTHELLO

> That's not so good now.

IAGO

> What,
> If I had said I had seen him do you wrong?
> Or heard him say, — as knaves be such abroad,
> Who having, by their own importunate suit,
> Or voluntary dotage of some mistress,
> Convinced or supplied them, cannot choose
> But they must blab —

OTHELLO

> Hath he said any thing?

IAGO

> He hath, my lord; but be you well assured,
> No more than he'll unswear.

OTHELLO

What hath he said?

IAGO

'Faith, that he did — I know not what he did.

OTHELLO

What? what?

IAGO

Lie —

OTHELLO

With her?

IAGO

With her, on her; what you will.

OTHELLO

Lie with her! lie on her! We say lie on her, when
they belie her. Lie with her! that's fulsome.
— Handkerchief — confessions — handkerchief! — To
confess, and be hanged for his labour; — first, to be
hanged, and then to confess. — I tremble at it.
Nature would not invest herself in such shadowing
passion without some instruction. It is not words
that shake me thus. Pish! Noses, ears, and lips.
— Is't possible? — Confess — handkerchief! — O devil! —

(Falls in a trance.)

IAGO

Work on,
My medicine, work! Thus credulous fools are caught;
And many worthy and chaste dames even thus,
All guiltless, meet reproach. What, ho! my lord!
My lord, I say! Othello!

THE WINTER'S TALE

Act 1, Scene 2
2 Characters: 2 male
Leontes, Camillo

Leontes wants to know if Camillo has seen the signs that Leontes's wife, Hermione, is having an adulterous affair.

—◆—

A room of state in Leontes's palace.

LEONTES
Camillo, this great sir will yet stay longer.

CAMILLO
You had much ado to make his anchor hold:
When you cast out, it still came home.

LEONTES
Didst note it?

CAMILLO
He would not stay at your petitions: made
His business more material.

LEONTES
Didst perceive it?

(Aside.) They're here with me already, whispering, rounding
'Sicilia is a so-forth':'tis far gone,
When I shall gust it last. How came't, Camillo,
That he did stay?

CAMILLO

    At the good queen's entreaty.

LEONTES

    At the queen's be't: 'good' should be pertinent
    But, so it is, it is not. Was this taken
    By any understanding pate but thine?
    For thy conceit is soaking, will draw in
    More than the common blocks: not noted, is't,
    But of the finer natures? by some severals
    Of head-piece extraordinary? lower messes
    Perchance are to this business purblind? say.

CAMILLO

    Business, my lord! I think most understand
    Bohemia stays here longer.

LEONTES

    Ha!

CAMILLO

    Stays here longer.

LEONTES

    Ay, but why?

CAMILLO

    To satisfy your highness and the entreaties
    Of our most gracious mistress.

LEONTES

    Satisfy!
    The entreaties of your mistress! satisfy!
    Let that suffice. I have trusted thee, Camillo,
    With all the nearest things to my heart, as well
    My chamber-councils, wherein, priest-like, thou

Hast cleansed my bosom, I from thee departed
Thy penitent reform'd: but we have been
Deceived in thy integrity, deceived
In that which seems so.

CAMILLO

Be it forbid, my lord!

LEONTES

To bide upon't, thou art not honest, or,
If thou inclinest that way, thou art a coward,
Which hoxes honesty behind, restraining
From course required; or else thou must be counted
A servant grafted in my serious trust
And therein negligent; or else a fool
That seest a game play'd home, the rich stake drawn,
And takest it all for jest.

CAMILLO

My gracious lord,
I may be negligent, foolish and fearful;
In every one of these no man is free,
But that his negligence, his folly, fear,
Among the infinite doings of the world,
Sometime puts forth. In your affairs, my lord,
If ever I were wilful-negligent,
It was my folly; if industriously
I play'd the fool, it was my negligence,
Not weighing well the end; if ever fearful
To do a thing, where I the issue doubted,
Where of the execution did cry out
Against the non-performance, 'twas a fear
Which oft infects the wisest: these, my lord,
Are such allow'd infirmities that honesty
Is never free of. But, beseech your grace,
Be plainer with me; let me know my trespass

By its own visage: if I then deny it,
'Tis none of mine.

LEONTES

    Ha' not you seen, Camillo, —
    But that's past doubt, you have, or your eye-glass
    Is thicker than a cuckold's horn, — or heard, —
    For to a vision so apparent rumour
    Cannot be mute, — or thought, — for cogitation
    Resides not in that man that does not think, —
    My wife is slippery? If thou wilt confess,
    Or else be impudently negative,
    To have nor eyes nor ears nor thought, then say
    My wife's a hobby-horse, deserves a name
    As rank as any flax-wench that puts to
    Before her troth-plight: say't and justify't.

CAMILLO

    I would not be a stander-by to hear
    My sovereign mistress clouded so, without
    My present vengeance taken: 'shrew my heart,
    You never spoke what did become you less
    Than this; which to reiterate were sin
    As deep as that, though true.

LEONTES

    Is whispering nothing?
    Is leaning cheek to cheek? is meeting noses?
    Kissing with inside lip? stopping the career
    Of laughing with a sigh? — a note infallible
    Of breaking honesty — horsing foot on foot?
    Skulking in corners? wishing clocks more swift?
    Hours, minutes? noon, midnight? and all eyes
    Blind with the pin and web but theirs, theirs only,
    That would unseen be wicked? is this nothing?
    Why, then the world and all that's in't is nothing;

The covering sky is nothing; Bohemia nothing;
My wife is nothing; nor nothing have these nothings,
If this be nothing.

CAMILLO

Good my lord, be cured
Of this diseased opinion, and betimes;
For 'tis most dangerous.

LEONTES

Say it be, 'tis true.

CAMILLO

No, no, my lord.

LEONTES

It is; you lie, you lie:
I say thou liest, Camillo, and I hate thee,
Pronounce thee a gross lout, a mindless slave,
Or else a hovering temporizer, that
Canst with thine eyes at once see good and evil,
Inclining to them both: were my wife's liver
Infected as her life, she would not live
The running of one glass.

CAMILLO

Who does infect her?

LEONTES

Why, he that wears her like a medal, hanging
About his neck, Bohemia: who, if I
Had servants true about me, that bare eyes
To see alike mine honour as their profits,
Their own particular thrifts, they would do that
Which should undo more doing: ay, and thou,
His cupbearer, — whom I from meaner form

Have benched and reared to worship, who mayst see
Plainly as heaven sees earth and earth sees heaven,
How I am galled, — mightst bespice a cup,
To give mine enemy a lasting wink;
Which draught to me were cordial.

CAMILLO

Sir, my lord,
I could do this, and that with no rash potion,
But with a lingering dram that should not work
Maliciously like poison: but I cannot
Believe this crack to be in my dread mistress,
So sovereignly being honourable.
I have loved thee, —

LEONTES

Make that thy question, and go rot!
Dost think I am so muddy, so unsettled,
To appoint myself in this vexation, sully
The purity and whiteness of my sheets,
Which to preserve is sleep, which being spotted
Is goads, thorns, nettles, tails of wasps,
Give scandal to the blood o' the prince my son,
Who I do think is mine and love as mine,
Without ripe moving to't? Would I do this?
Could man so blench?

CAMILLO

I must believe you, sir:
I do; and will fetch off Bohemia for't;
Provided that, when he's removed, your highness
Will take again your queen as yours at first,
Even for your son's sake; and thereby for sealing
The injury of tongues in courts and kingdoms
Known and allied to yours.

LEONTES

Thou dost advise me
Even so as I mine own course have set down:
I'll give no blemish to her honour, none.

CAMILLO

My lord,
Go then; and with a countenance as clear
As friendship wears at feasts, keep with Bohemia
And with your queen. I am his cupbearer:
If from me he have wholesome beverage,
Account me not your servant.

LEONTES

This is all:
Do't and thou hast the one half of my heart;
Do't not, thou split'st thine own.

CAMILLO

I'll do't, my lord.

LEONTES

I will seem friendly, as thou hast advised me.

(Exit.)

TWO GENTLEMEN OF VERONA
Act 4, Scene 4
2 Characters: 2 female (plus attendants)
Julia, Silvia

Julia is in love with Proteus, who has fallen in love with Silvia. Disguised as a boy, Julia is hired by Proteus as a messenger. Proteus tells her to take a ring to Silvia as a token of his affection; it is the ring that she (as Julia) had given him. Dutifully, Julia goes to Silvia. Silvia refuses the ring and scoffs at Proteus' suit, expressing sorrow for Julia, unaware of who the messenger is.

<hr />

Milan. Outside the Duke's palace, under Silvia's chamber.
Enter SILVIA.

JULIA
> Gentlewoman, good day! I pray you, be my mean
> To bring me where to speak with Madam Silvia.

SILVIA
> What would you with her, if that I be she?

JULIA
> If you be she, I do entreat your patience
> To hear me speak the message I am sent on.

SILVIA
> From whom?

JULIA
> From my master, Sir Proteus, madam.

SILVIA
> O, he sends you for a picture.

JULIA

    Ay, madam.

SILVIA

    Ursula, bring my picture here.
    Go give your master this: tell him from me,
    One Julia, that his changing thoughts forget,
    Would better fit his chamber than this shadow.

JULIA

    Madam, please you peruse this letter. —
    Pardon me, madam; I have unadvised
    Deliver'd you a paper that I should not:
    This is the letter to your ladyship.

SILVIA

    I pray thee, let me look on that again.

JULIA

    It may not be; good madam, pardon me.

SILVIA

    There, hold!
    I will not look upon your master's lines:
    I know they are stuff'd with protestations
    And full of new-found oaths; which he will break
    As easily as I do tear his paper.

JULIA

    Madam, he sends your ladyship this ring.

SILVIA

    The more shame for him that he sends it me;
    For I have heard him say a thousand times
    His Julia gave it him at his departure.
    Though his false finger have profaned the ring,
    Mine shall not do his Julia so much wrong.

JULIA

She thanks you.

SILVIA

What say'st thou?

JULIA

I thank you, madam, that you tender her.
Poor gentlewoman! my master wrongs her much.

SILVIA

Dost thou know her?

JULIA

Almost as well as I do know myself:
To think upon her woes I do protest
That I have wept a hundred several times.

SILVIA

Belike she thinks that Proteus hath forsook her.

JULIA

I think she doth; and that's her cause of sorrow.

SILVIA

Is she not passing fair?

JULIA

She hath been fairer, madam, than she is:
When she did think my master loved her well,
She, in my judgment, was as fair as you:
But since she did neglect her looking-glass
And threw her sun-expelling mask away,
The air hath starved the roses in her cheeks
And pinch'd the lily-tincture of her face,
That now she is become as black as I.

SILVIA

How tall was she?

JULIA

About my stature; for at Pentecost,
When all our pageants of delight were play'd,
Our youth got me to play the woman's part,
And I was trimm'd in Madam Julia's gown,
Which served me as fit, by all men's judgments,
As if the garment had been made for me:
Therefore I know she is about my height.
And at that time I made her weep agood,
For I did play a lamentable part:
Madam, 'twas Ariadne passioning
For Theseus' perjury and unjust flight;
Which I so lively acted with my tears
That my poor mistress, moved therewithal,
Wept bitterly; and would I might be dead
If I in thought felt not her very sorrow!

SILVIA

She is beholding to thee, gentle youth.
Alas, poor lady, desolate and left!
I weep myself to think upon thy words.
Here, youth, there is my purse; I give thee this
For thy sweet mistress' sake, because thou lovest her.
Farewell.

(Exit SILVIA.)

JULIA

And she shall thank you for't, if e'er you know her.
A virtuous gentlewoman, mild and beautiful
I hope my master's suit will be but cold,
Since she respects my mistress' love so much.
Alas, how love can trifle with itself!

Here is her picture: let me see; I think,
If I had such a tire, this face of mine
Were full as lovely as is this of hers:
And yet the painter flatter'd her a little,
Unless I flatter with myself too much.
Her hair is auburn, mine is perfect yellow:
If that be all the difference in his love,
I'll get me such a colour'd periwig.
Her eyes are grey as glass, and so are mine:
Ay, but her forehead's low, and mine's as high.
What should it be that he respects in her
But I can make respective in myself,
If this fond Love were not a blinded god?
Come, shadow, come and take this shadow up,
For 'tis thy rival. O thou senseless form,
Thou shalt be worshipp'd, kiss'd, loved and adored!
And, were there sense in his idolatry,
My substance should be statue in thy stead.
I'll use thee kindly for thy mistress' sake,
That used me so; or else, by Jove I vow,
I should have scratch'd out your unseeing eyes
To make my master out of love with thee!

(Exit.)

THE COMEDY OF ERRORS

Act 2, Scene 1
2 Characters: 2 female
Adriana, Luciana

Adriana, wife of Antipholus of Ephesus, is irritated by her husband's lateness and complains to her sister, Luciana. The scene ends as Luciana sees Antipholus' servant, Dromio, arriving and suggests Antipholus is also near.

―――――⇒◦⇐―――――

The house of Antipholus of Ephesus. Enter ADRIANA and LUCIANA.

ADRIANA
> Neither my husband nor the slave return'd,
> That in such haste I sent to seek his master!
> Sure, Luciana, it is two o'clock.

LUCIANA
> Perhaps some merchant hath invited him,
> And from the mart he's somewhere gone to dinner.
> Good sister, let us dine and never fret:
> A man is master of his liberty:
> Time is their master, and, when they see time,
> They'll go or come: if so, be patient, sister.

ADRIANA
> Why should their liberty than ours be more?

LUCIANA
> Because their business still lies out o' door.

ADRIANA
> Look, when I serve him so, he takes it ill.

LUCIANA

O, know he is the bridle of your will.

ADRIANA

There's none but asses will be bridled so.

LUCIANA

Why, headstrong liberty is lash'd with woe.
There's nothing situate under heaven's eye
But hath his bound, in earth, in sea, in sky:
The beasts, the fishes, and the winged fowls,
Are their males' subjects and at their controls:
Men, more divine, the masters of all these,
Lords of the wide world and wild watery seas,
Indued with intellectual sense and souls,
Of more preeminence than fish and fowls,
Are masters to their females, and their lords:
Then let your will attend on their accords.

ADRIANA

This servitude makes you to keep unwed.

LUCIANA

Not this, but troubles of the marriage-bed.

ADRIANA

But, were you wedded, you would bear some sway.

LUCIANA

Ere I learn love, I'll practise to obey.

ADRIANA

How if your husband start some other where?

LUCIANA

Till he come home again, I would forbear.

ADRIANA

    Patience unmoved! no marvel though she pause;
    They can be meek that have no other cause.
    A wretched soul, bruised with adversity,
    We bid be quiet when we hear it cry;
    But were we burdened with like weight of pain,
    As much or more would we ourselves complain:
    So thou, that hast no unkind mate to grieve thee,
    With urging helpless patience wouldst relieve me,
    But, if thou live to see like right bereft,
    This fool-begg'd patience in thee will be left.

LUCIANA

    Well, I will marry one day, but to try.
    Here comes your man; now is your husband nigh.

SCENES FOR
THREE CHARACTERS

ANTONY AND CLEOPATRA

Act 2, Scene 5
3 Characters: 1 male, 2 female
Cleopatra (F), Charmian (F), Messenger (M)

Eager for news about Antony, Cleopatra is so excited when a messenger from Rome arrives that she keeps interrupting him and preventing him from telling what he has to say. When she hears Antony has married Octavia, she becomes furious and attacks the messenger.

⟫―◦―⟪

Alexandria. Cleopatra's palace.

CLEOPATRA
> That time, — O times! —
> I laugh'd him out of patience; and that night
> I laugh'd him into patience; and next morn,
> Ere the ninth hour, I drunk him to his bed;
> Then put my tires and mantles on him, whilst
> I wore his sword Philippan.

> *(Enter a MESSENGER.)*

> O, from Italy
> Ram thou thy fruitful tidings in mine ears,
> That long time have been barren.

MESSENGER
> Madam, madam, —

CLEOPATRA
> Antonius dead! — If thou say so, villain,
> Thou kill'st thy mistress: but well and free,
> If thou so yield him, there is gold, and here

My bluest veins to kiss; a hand that kings
Have lipp'd, and trembled kissing.

MESSENGER
    First, madam, he is well.

CLEOPATRA
    Why, there's more gold.
    But, sirrah, mark, we use
    To say the dead are well: bring it to that,
    The gold I give thee will I melt and pour
    Down thy ill-uttering throat.

MESSENGER
    Good madam, hear me.

CLEOPATRA
    Well, go to, I will;
    But there's no goodness in thy face: if Antony
    Be free and healthful, — so tart a favour
    To trumpet such good tidings! If not well,
    Thou shouldst come like a Fury crown'd with snakes,
    Not like a formal man.

MESSENGER
    Will't please you hear me?

CLEOPATRA
    I have a mind to strike thee ere thou speak'st:
    Yet if thou say Antony lives, is well,
    Or friends with Caesar, or not captive to him,
    I'll set thee in a shower of gold, and hail
    Rich pearls upon thee.

MESSENGER
    Madam, he's well.

CLEOPATRA
    Well said.

MESSENGER
    And friends with Caesar.

CLEOPATRA
    Thou'rt an honest man.

MESSENGER
    Caesar and he are greater friends than ever.

CLEOPATRA
    Make thee a fortune from me.

MESSENGER
    But yet, madam, —

CLEOPATRA
    I do not like 'But yet,' it does allay
    The good precedence; fie upon 'But yet'!
    'But yet' is as a gaoler to bring forth
    Some monstrous malefactor. Prithee, friend,
    Pour out the pack of matter to mine ear,
    The good and bad together: he's friends with Caesar:
    In state of health thou say'st; and thou say'st free.

MESSENGER
    Free, madam! no; I made no such report:
    He's bound unto Octavia.

CLEOPATRA
    For what good turn?

MESSENGER
    For the best turn i' the bed.

CLEOPATRA
    I am pale, Charmian.

MESSENGER
    Madam, he's married to Octavia.

CLEOPATRA
    The most infectious pestilence upon thee!

    (Strikes him down.)

MESSENGER
    Good madam, patience.

CLEOPATRA
    What say you? Hence,

    (Strikes him again.)

    Horrible villain! or I'll spurn thine eyes
    Like balls before me; I'll unhair thy head:

    (She hales him up and down.)

    Thou shalt be whipp'd with wire, and stew'd in brine,
    Smarting in lingering pickle.

MESSENGER
    Gracious madam,
    I that do bring the news made not the match.

CLEOPATRA
    Say 'tis not so, a province I will give thee,
    And make thy fortunes proud: the blow thou hadst
    Shall make thy peace for moving me to rage;
    And I will boot thee with what gift beside
    Thy modesty can beg.

MESSENGER

He's married, madam.

CLEOPATRA

Rogue, thou hast lived too long.

(Draws a knife.)

MESSENGER

Nay, then I'll run.
What mean you, madam? I have made no fault.

(Exit.)

CHARMIAN

Good madam, keep yourself within yourself:
The man is innocent.

CLEOPATRA

Some innocents 'scape not the thunderbolt.
Melt Egypt into Nile! and kindly creatures
Turn all to serpents! Call the slave again:
Though I am mad, I will not bite him: call.

CHARMIAN

He is afeard to come.

CLEOPATRA

I will not hurt him.

(Exit CHARMIAN.)

These hands do lack nobility, that they strike
A meaner than myself; since I myself
Have given myself the cause.

(Re-enter CHARMIAN and MESSENGER.)

Come hither, sir.
Though it be honest, it is never good
To bring bad news: give to a gracious message.
An host of tongues; but let ill tidings tell
Themselves when they be felt.

MESSENGER

I have done my duty.

CLEOPATRA

Is he married?
I cannot hate thee worser than I do,
If thou again say 'Yes.'

MESSENGER

He's married, madam.

CLEOPATRA

The gods confound thee! dost thou hold there still?

MESSENGER

Should I lie, madam?

CLEOPATRA

O, I would thou didst,
So half my Egypt were submerged and made
A cistern for scaled snakes! Go, get thee hence:
Hadst thou Narcissus in thy face, to me
Thou wouldst appear most ugly. He is married?

MESSENGER

I crave your highness' pardon.

CLEOPATRA

He is married?

MESSENGER

    Take no offence that I would not offend you:
    To punish me for what you make me do.
    Seems much unequal: he's married to Octavia.

CLEOPATRA

    O, that his fault should make a knave of thee,
    That art not what thou'rt sure of! Get thee hence:
    The merchandise which thou hast brought from Rome
    Are all too dear for me: lie they upon thy hand,
    And be undone by 'em!

(Exit MESSENGER.)

AS YOU LIKE IT
Act 3, Scene 5
3 Characters: 2 female, 1 male
Rosalind (F), Phebe (F), Silvius (M)

Silvius tells Phebe he loves her, but she dismisses him. Rosalind, disguised as the boy Ganymede, intervenes and chides Phebe for mistreating Silvius. Phebe is smitten by Ganymede and writes "him" a letter that Silvius, not knowing her feelings, agrees to take to Ganymede.

Another part of the forest. Enter SILVIUS and PHEBE.

SILVIUS
    Sweet Phebe, do not scorn me; do not, Phebe;
    Say that you love me not, but say not so
    In bitterness. The common executioner,
    Whose heart the accustom'd sight of death makes hard,
    Falls not the axe upon the humbled neck
    But first begs pardon: will you sterner be
    Than he that dies and lives by bloody drops?

(Enter ROSALIND.)

PHEBE
    I would not be thy executioner:
    I fly thee, for I would not injure thee.
    Thou tell'st me there is murder in mine eye:
    'Tis pretty, sure, and very probable,
    That eyes, that are the frail'st and softest things,
    Who shut their coward gates on atomies,
    Should be call'd tyrants, butchers, murderers!
    Now I do frown on thee with all my heart;

And if mine eyes can wound, now let them kill thee:
Now counterfeit to swoon; why now fall down;
Or if thou canst not, O, for shame, for shame,
Lie not, to say mine eyes are murderers!
Now show the wound mine eye hath made in thee:
Scratch thee but with a pin, and there remains
Some scar of it; lean but upon a rush,
The cicatrice and capable impressure
Thy palm some moment keeps; but now mine eyes,
Which I have darted at thee, hurt thee not,
Nor, I am sure, there is no force in eyes
That can do hurt.

SILVIUS
O dear Phebe,
If ever, — as that ever may be near, —
You meet in some fresh cheek the power of fancy,
Then shall you know the wounds invisible
That love's keen arrows make.

PHEBE
But till that time
Come not thou near me: and when that time comes,
Afflict me with thy mocks, pity me not;
As till that time I shall not pity thee.

ROSALIND
And why, I pray you? Who might be your mother,
That you insult, exult, and all at once,
Over the wretched? What though you have no beauty, —
As, by my faith, I see no more in you
Than without candle may go dark to bed —
Must you be therefore proud and pitiless?
Why, what means this? Why do you look on me?
I see no more in you than in the ordinary
Of nature's sale-work. 'Od's my little life,

I think she means to tangle my eyes too!
No, faith, proud mistress, hope not after it:
'Tis not your inky brows, your black silk hair,
Your bugle eyeballs, nor your cheek of cream,
That can entame my spirits to your worship.
You foolish shepherd, wherefore do you follow her,
Like foggy south puffing with wind and rain?
You are a thousand times a properer man
Than she a woman: 'tis such fools as you
That makes the world full of ill-favour'd children:
'Tis not her glass, but you, that flatters her;
And out of you she sees herself more proper
Than any of her lineaments can show her.
But, mistress, know yourself: down on your knees,
And thank heaven, fasting, for a good man's love:
For I must tell you friendly in your ear,
Sell when you can: you are not for all markets:
Cry the man mercy; love him; take his offer:
Foul is most foul, being foul to be a scoffer.
So take her to thee, shepherd: fare you well.

PHEBE

    Sweet youth, I pray you, chide a year together:
    I had rather hear you chide than this man woo.

ROSALIND

    He's fallen in love with your foulness and she'll
    fall in love with my anger. If it be so, as fast as
    she answers thee with frowning looks, I'll sauce her
    with bitter words. Why look you so upon me?

PHEBE

    For no ill will I bear you.

ROSALIND

    I pray you, do not fall in love with me,

For I am falser than vows made in wine:
Besides, I like you not. If you will know my house,
'Tis at the tuft of olives here hard by.
Will you go, sister? Shepherd, ply her hard.
Come, sister. Shepherdess, look on him better,
And be not proud: though all the world could see,
None could be so abused in sight as he.
Come, to our flock.

(Exeunt ROSALIND.)

PHEBE

Dead Shepherd, now I find thy saw of might,
'Who ever loved that loved not at first sight?'

SILVIUS

Sweet Phebe, —

PHEBE

Ha, what say'st thou, Silvius?

SILVIUS

Sweet Phebe, pity me.

PHEBE

Why, I am sorry for thee, gentle Silvius.

SILVIUS

Wherever sorrow is, relief would be:
If you do sorrow at my grief in love,
By giving love your sorrow and my grief
Were both extermined.

PHEBE

Thou hast my love: is not that neighbourly?

SILVIUS

I would have you.

PHEBE

Why, that were covetousness.
Silvius, the time was that I hated thee,
And yet it is not that I bear thee love;
But since that thou canst talk of love so well,
Thy company, which erst was irksome to me,
I will endure, and I'll employ thee too:
But do not look for further recompense
Than thine own gladness that thou art employ'd.

SILVIUS

So holy and so perfect is my love,
And I in such a poverty of grace,
That I shall think it a most plenteous crop
To glean the broken ears after the man
That the main harvest reaps: loose now and then
A scatter'd smile, and that I'll live upon.

PHEBE

Know'st now the youth that spoke to me erewhile?

SILVIUS

Not very well, but I have met him oft;
And he hath bought the cottage and the bounds
That the old carlot once was master of.

PHEBE

Think not I love him, though I ask for him:
'Tis but a peevish boy; yet he talks well;
But what care I for words? yet words do well
When he that speaks them pleases those that hear.
It is a pretty youth: not very pretty:
But, sure, he's proud, and yet his pride becomes him:

He'll make a proper man: the best thing in him
Is his complexion; and faster than his tongue
Did make offence his eye did heal it up.
He is not very tall; yet for his years he's tall:
His leg is but so so; and yet 'tis well:
There was a pretty redness in his lip,
A little riper and more lusty red
Than that mix'd in his cheek; 'twas just the difference
Between the constant red and mingled damask.
There be some women, Silvius, had they mark'd him
In parcels as I did, would have gone near
To fall in love with him; but, for my part,
I love him not nor hate him not; and yet
I have more cause to hate him than to love him:
For what had he to do to chide at me?
He said mine eyes were black and my hair black:
And, now I am remember'd, scorn'd at me:
I marvel why I answer'd not again:
But that's all one; omittance is no quittance.
I'll write to him a very taunting letter,
And thou shalt bear it: wilt thou, Silvius?

SILVIUS
    Phebe, with all my heart.

PHEBE
    I'll write it straight;
    The matter's in my head and in my heart:
    I will be bitter with him and passing short.
    Go with me, Silvius.

    (Exeunt.)

CYMBELINE

Act 1, Scene 1
3 Characters: 2 female, 1 male
Queen (F), Imogen (F), Posthumus Leonatus (M)

Cymbeline, King of Britain, is furious that his daughter, Imogen, has secretly married the impoverished Posthumus Leonatus. Cymbeline has ordered Posthumus Leonatus banished from the kingdom. The Queen promises to change the King's mind, and the two lovers exchange keepsakes, a ring and a bracelet.

———➤●◄———

Britain. The garden of Cymbeline's palace. Enter the QUEEN, POSTHUMUS LEONATUS, and IMOGEN.

QUEEN
　　No, be assured you shall not find me, daughter,
　　After the slander of most stepmothers,
　　Evil-eyed unto you: you're my prisoner, but
　　Your gaoler shall deliver you the keys
　　That lock up your restraint. For you, Posthumus,
　　So soon as I can win the offended king,
　　I will be known your advocate: marry, yet
　　The fire of rage is in him, and 'twere good
　　You lean'd unto his sentence with what patience
　　Your wisdom may inform you.

POSTHUMUS LEONATUS
　　Please your highness,
　　I will from hence to-day.

QUEEN
　　You know the peril.
　　I'll fetch a turn about the garden, pitying

The pangs of barr'd affections, though the king
Hath charged you should not speak together.

(Exit.)

IMOGEN
O dissembling courtesy! How fine this tyrant
Can tickle where she wounds! My dearest husband,
I something fear my father's wrath; but nothing —
Always reserved my holy duty — what
His rage can do on me: you must be gone;
And I shall here abide the hourly shot
Of angry eyes, not comforted to live,
But that there is this jewel in the world
That I may see again.

POSTHUMUS LEONATUS
My queen! my mistress!
O lady, weep no more, lest I give cause
To be suspected of more tenderness
Than doth become a man. I will remain
The loyal'st husband that did e'er plight troth:
My residence in Rome at one Philario's,
Who to my father was a friend, to me
Known but by letter: thither write, my queen,
And with mine eyes I'll drink the words you send,
Though ink be made of gall.

(Re-enter QUEEN.)

QUEEN
Be brief, I pray you:
If the king come, I shall incur I know not
How much of his displeasure.

(Aside.) Yet I'll move him

To walk this way: I never do him wrong,
But he does buy my injuries, to be friends;
Pays dear for my offences.

(Exit.)

POSTHUMUS LEONATUS
    Should we be taking leave
    As long a term as yet we have to live,
    The loathness to depart would grow. Adieu!

IMOGEN
    Nay, stay a little:
    Were you but riding forth to air yourself,
    Such parting were too petty. Look here, love;
    This diamond was my mother's: take it, heart;
    But keep it till you woo another wife,
    When Imogen is dead.

POSTHUMUS LEONATUS
    How, how! another?
    You gentle gods, give me but this I have,
    And sear up my embracements from a next
    With bonds of death!

(Putting on the ring.)

    Remain, remain thou here
    While sense can keep it on. And, sweetest, fairest,
    As I my poor self did exchange for you,
    To your so infinite loss, so in our trifles
    I still win of you: for my sake wear this;
    It is a manacle of love; I'll place it
    Upon this fairest prisoner.

(Putting a bracelet upon her arm.)

IMOGEN
O the gods!
When shall we see again?

MACBETH

Act 5, Scene 1
3 Characters: 2 female, 1 male
Lady Macbeth (F), Gentlewoman (F), Doctor (M)

Lady Macbeth's servant (Gentlewoman) tells the doctor about Lady Macbeth's strange nocturnal behavior. Lady Macbeth appears — sleepwalking and trying to wash away invisible bloodstains from her hands while divulging her murderous plots.

——➤◦◄——

Dunsinane. Ante-room in the castle. Enter a DOCTOR of physic and a GENTLEWOMAN.

DOCTOR

I have two nights watched with you, but can perceive
no truth in your report. When was it she last walked?

GENTLEWOMAN

Since his majesty went into the field, I have seen
her rise from her bed, throw her night-gown upon
her, unlock her closet, take forth paper, fold it,
write upon't, read it, afterwards seal it, and again
return to bed; yet all this while in a most fast sleep.

DOCTOR

A great perturbation in nature, to receive at once
the benefit of sleep, and do the effects of
watching! In this slumbery agitation, besides her
walking and other actual performances, what, at any
time, have you heard her say?

GENTLEWOMAN

That, sir, which I will not report after her.

DOCTOR

You may to me: and 'tis most meet you should.

GENTLEWOMAN

Neither to you nor any one; having no witness to
confirm my speech.

(Enter LADY MACBETH, with a taper.)

Lo you, here she comes! This is her very guise;
and, upon my life, fast asleep. Observe her; stand close.

DOCTOR

How came she by that light?

GENTLEWOMAN

Why, it stood by her: she has light by her
continually; 'tis her command.

DOCTOR

You see, her eyes are open.

GENTLEWOMAN

Ay, but their sense is shut.

DOCTOR

What is it she does now? Look, how she rubs her hands.

GENTLEWOMAN

It is an accustomed action with her, to seem thus
washing her hands: I have known her continue in
this a quarter of an hour.

LADY MACBETH

Yet here's a spot.

DOCTOR

> Hark! she speaks: I will set down what comes from
> her, to satisfy my remembrance the more strongly.

LADY MACBETH

> Out, damned spot! out, I say! — One: two: why,
> then, 'tis time to do't. — Hell is murky! — Fie, my
> lord, fie! a soldier, and afeard? What need we
> fear who knows it, when none can call our power to
> account? — Yet who would have thought the old man
> to have had so much blood in him.

DOCTOR

> Do you mark that?

LADY MACBETH

> The thane of Fife had a wife: where is she now? —
> What, will these hands ne'er be clean? — No more o'
> that, my lord, no more o' that: you mar all with
> this starting.

DOCTOR

> Go to, go to; you have known what you should not.

GENTLEWOMAN

> She has spoke what she should not, I am sure of
> that: heaven knows what she has known.

LADY MACBETH

> Here's the smell of the blood still: all the
> perfumes of Arabia will not sweeten this little
> hand. Oh, oh, oh!

DOCTOR

> What a sigh is there! The heart is sorely charged.

GENTLEWOMAN

I would not have such a heart in my bosom for the dignity of the whole body.

DOCTOR

Well, well, well, —

GENTLEWOMAN

Pray God it be, sir.

DOCTOR

This disease is beyond my practise: yet I have known those which have walked in their sleep who have died holily in their beds.

LADY MACBETH

Wash your hands, put on your nightgown; look not so pale. — I tell you yet again, Banquo's buried; he cannot come out on's grave.

DOCTOR

Even so?

LADY MACBETH

To bed, to bed! there's knocking at the gate: come, come, come, come, give me your hand. What's done cannot be undone. — To bed, to bed, to bed!

(Exit.)

DOCTOR

Will she go now to bed?

GENTLEWOMAN

Directly.

DOCTOR

> Foul whisperings are abroad: unnatural deeds
> Do breed unnatural troubles: infected minds
> To their deaf pillows will discharge their secrets:
> More needs she the divine than the physician.
> God, God forgive us all! Look after her;
> Remove from her the means of all annoyance,
> And still keep eyes upon her. So, good night:
> My mind she has mated, and amazed my sight.
> I think, but dare not speak.

GENTLEWOMAN

> Good night, good doctor.

> *(Exeunt.)*

THE COMEDY OF ERRORS

Act 4, Scene 2

3 Characters: 2 female, 1 male

Adriana (F), Luciana (F), Dromio of Syracuse (M)

Luciana tells her sister, Adriana, that Adriana's husband, Antipholus of Ephesus, has tried to woo her (Luciana). The suitor is the husband's identical twin — Antipholus of Syracuse, who is unknown to the two women. A servant, Dromio of Syracuse, bursts in saying that Antipholus of Ephesus has been arrested and asks Adriana to give him bail money. Dromio of Syracuse, of course, thinks that it is his master — Antipholus of Syracuse — who has been arrested, and the women think that Dromio of Syracuse is their servant, Dromio of Ephesus.

<hr/>

The house of Antipholus of Ephesus. Enter ADRIANA and LUCIANA.

ADRIANA

> Ah, Luciana, did he tempt thee so?
> Mightst thou perceive austerely in his eye
> That he did plead in earnest? yea or no?
> Look'd he or red or pale, or sad or merrily?
> What observation madest thou in this case
> Of his heart's meteors tilting in his face?

LUCIANA

> First he denied you had in him no right.

ADRIANA

> He meant he did me none; the more my spite.

LUCIANA

> Then swore he that he was a stranger here.

ADRIANA

And true he swore, though yet forsworn he were.

LUCIANA

Then pleaded I for you.

ADRIANA

And what said he?

LUCIANA

That love I begg'd for you he begg'd of me.

ADRIANA

With what persuasion did he tempt thy love?

LUCIANA

With words that in an honest suit might move.
First he did praise my beauty, then my speech.

ADRIANA

Didst speak him fair?

LUCIANA

Have patience, I beseech.

ADRIANA

I cannot, nor I will not, hold me still;
My tongue, though not my heart, shall have his will.
He is deformed, crooked, old and sere,
Ill-faced, worse bodied, shapeless everywhere;
Vicious, ungentle, foolish, blunt, unkind;
Stigmatical in making, worse in mind.

LUCIANA

Who would be jealous then of such a one?
No evil lost is wail'd when it is gone.

ADRIANA

Ah, but I think him better than I say,
And yet would herein others' eyes were worse.
Far from her nest the lapwing cries away:
My heart prays for him, though my tongue do curse.

(Enter DROMIO of Syracuse.)

DROMIO OF SYRACUSE

Here! go; the desk, the purse! sweet, now, make haste.

LUCIANA

How hast thou lost thy breath?

DROMIO OF SYRACUSE

By running fast.

ADRIANA

Where is thy master, Dromio? is he well?

DROMIO OF SYRACUSE

No, he's in Tartar limbo, worse than hell.
A devil in an everlasting garment hath him;
One whose hard heart is button'd up with steel;
A fiend, a fury, pitiless and rough;
A wolf, nay, worse, a fellow all in buff;
A back-friend, a shoulder-clapper, one that
countermands
The passages of alleys, creeks and narrow lands;
A hound that runs counter and yet draws dryfoot well;
One that before the judgement carries poor souls to hell.

ADRIANA

Why, man, what is the matter?

DROMIO OF SYRACUSE

    I do not know the matter: he is 'rested on the case.

ADRIANA

    What, is he arrested? Tell me at whose suit.

DROMIO OF SYRACUSE

    I know not at whose suit he is arrested well;
    But he's in a suit of buff which 'rested him, that can I tell.
    Will you send him, mistress, redemption, the money in his desk?

ADRIANA

    Go fetch it, sister.

    (Exit LUCIANA.)

    This I wonder at,
    That he, unknown to me, should be in debt.
    Tell me, was he arrested on a band?

DROMIO OF SYRACUSE

    Not on a band, but on a stronger thing;
    A chain, a chain! Do you not hear it ring?

ADRIANA

    What, the chain?

DROMIO OF SYRACUSE

    No, no, the bell: 'tis time that I were gone:
    It was two ere I left him, and now the clock
    strikes one.

ADRIANA

    The hours come back! that did I never hear.

DROMIO OF SYRACUSE

O, yes; if any hour meet a sergeant, a' turns back for
very fear.

ADRIANA

As if Time were in debt! how fondly dost thou reason!

DROMIO OF SYRACUSE

Time is a very bankrupt, and owes more than he's
worth, to season.
Nay, he's a thief too: have you not heard men say
That Time comes stealing on by night and day?
If Time be in debt and theft, and a sergeant in the way,
Hath he not reason to turn back an hour in a day?

(Re-enter LUCIANA with a purse.)

ADRIANA

Go, Dromio; there's the money, bear it straight;
And bring thy master home immediately.
Come, sister: I am press'd down with conceit —
Conceit, my comfort and my injury.

(Exeunt.)

THE TAMING OF THE SHREW
Act 2, Scene 1
3 Characters: 2 female, 1 male
Bianca (F), Katharina (F), Baptista (M)

Two sisters — sweet-tempered Bianca and ill-tempered Katharina —
quarrel because their father, Baptista, refuses to allow Bianca to be
married until a husband is found for Katharina.

———➤◦◄———

Padua. A room in Baptista's house. Enter KATHARINA and
BIANCA.

BIANCA

    Good sister, wrong me not, nor wrong yourself,
    To make a bondmaid and a slave of me;
    That I disdain: but for these other gawds,
    Unbind my hands, I'll pull them off myself,
    Yea, all my raiment, to my petticoat;
    Or what you will command me will I do,
    So well I know my duty to my elders.

KATHARINA

    Of all thy suitors, here I charge thee, tell
    Whom thou lovest best: see thou dissemble not.

BIANCA

    Believe me, sister, of all the men alive
    I never yet beheld that special face
    Which I could fancy more than any other.

KATHARINA

    Minion, thou liest. Is't not Hortensio?

BIANCA

    If you affect him, sister, here I swear
    I'll plead for you myself, but you shall have
    him.

KATHARINA

    O then, belike, you fancy riches more:
    You will have Gremio to keep you fair.

BIANCA

    Is it for him you do envy me so?
    Nay then you jest, and now I well perceive
    You have but jested with me all this while:
    I prithee, sister Kate, untie my hands.

KATHARINA

    If that be jest, then all the rest was so.

    (Strikes her.)
    (Enter BAPTISTA.)

BAPTISTA

    Why, how now, dame! whence grows this insolence?
    Bianca, stand aside. Poor girl! she weeps.
    Go ply thy needle; meddle not with her.
    For shame, thou helding of a devilish spirit,
    Why dost thou wrong her that did ne'er wrong thee?
    When did she cross thee with a bitter word?

KATHARINA

    Her silence flouts me, and I'll be revenged.

    (Flies after BIANCA.)

BAPTISTA

    What, in my sight? Bianca, get thee in.

(Exit BIANCA.)

KATHARINA

What, will you not suffer me? Nay, now I see
She is your treasure, she must have a husband;
I must dance bare-foot on her wedding day
And for your love to her lead apes in hell.
Talk not to me: I will go sit and weep
Till I can find occasion of revenge.

(Exit.)

TWELFTH NIGHT

Act 3, Scene 1
3 characters: 2 female, 1 male
Olivia (F), Viola (F), Sir Andrew (M)

Upon the Duke's command, Viola travels back to Olivia, encountering the clownish Sir Andrew. Olivia is infatuated by Viola, who she thinks is the boy-servant Cesario. Viola rejects Olivia's declaration of love and tries without success to press the Duke's cause.

Olivia's garden.

VIOLA
Most excellent accomplished lady, the heavens rain odours on you!

SIR ANDREW
That youth's a rare courtier: 'Rain odours'; well.

VIOLA
My matter hath no voice, to your own most pregnant and vouchsafed ear.

SIR ANDREW
'Odours,' 'pregnant' and 'vouchsafed:' I'll get 'em all three all ready.

OLIVIA
Let the garden door be shut, and leave me to my hearing. Give me your hand, sir.

VIOLA
My duty, madam, and most humble service.

OLIVIA

What is your name?

VIOLA

Cesario is your servant's name, fair princess.

OLIVIA

My servant, sir! 'Twas never merry world
Since lowly feigning was call'd compliment:
You're servant to the Count Orsino, youth.

VIOLA

And he is yours, and his must needs be yours:
Your servant's servant is your servant, madam.

OLIVIA

For him, I think not on him: for his thoughts,
Would they were blanks, rather than fill'd with me!

VIOLA

Madam, I come to whet your gentle thoughts
On his behalf.

OLIVIA

O, by your leave, I pray you,
I bade you never speak again of him:
But, would you undertake another suit,
I had rather hear you to solicit that
Than music from the spheres.

VIOLA

Dear lady, —

OLIVIA

Give me leave, beseech you. I did send,
After the last enchantment you did here,

A ring in chase of you: so did I abuse
Myself, my servant and, I fear me, you:
Under your hard construction must I sit,
To force that on you, in a shameful cunning,
Which you knew none of yours: what might you think?
Have you not set mine honour at the stake
And baited it with all the unmuzzled thoughts
That tyrannous heart can think? To one of your receiving
Enough is shown: a cypress, not a bosom,
Hideth my heart. So, let me hear you speak.

VIOLA

I pity you.

OLIVIA

That's a degree to love.

VIOLA

No, not a grize; for 'tis a vulgar proof,
That very oft we pity enemies.

OLIVIA

Why, then, methinks 'tis time to smile again.
O, world, how apt the poor are to be proud!
If one should be a prey, how much the better
To fall before the lion than the wolf!

(Clock strikes.)

The clock upbraids me with the waste of time.
Be not afraid, good youth, I will not have you:
And yet, when wit and youth is come to harvest,
Your were is alike to reap a proper man:
There lies your way, due west.

VIOLA

Then westward-ho! Grace and good disposition

Attend your ladyship!
You'll nothing, madam, to my lord by me?

OLIVIA
    Stay:
I prithee, tell me what thou thinkest of me.

VIOLA
    That you do think you are not what you are.

OLIVIA
    If I think so, I think the same of you.

VIOLA
    Then think you right: I am not what I am.

OLIVIA
    I would you were as I would have you be!

VIOLA
    Would it be better, madam, than I am?
    I wish it might, for now I am your fool.

OLIVIA
    O, what a deal of scorn looks beautiful
    In the contempt and anger of his lip!
    A murderous guilt shows not itself more soon
    Than love that would seem hid: love's night is noon.
    Cesario, by the roses of the spring,
    By maidhood, honour, truth and every thing,
    I love thee so, that, maugre all thy pride,
    Nor wit nor reason can my passion hide.
    Do not extort thy reasons from this clause,
    For that I woo, thou therefore hast no cause,
    But rather reason thus with reason fetter,
    Love sought is good, but given unsought better.

VIOLA

> By innocence I swear, and by my youth
> I have one heart, one bosom and one truth,
> And that no woman has; nor never none
> Shall mistress be of it, save I alone.
> And so adieu, good madam: never more
> Will I my master's tears to you deplore.

OLIVIA

> Yet come again; for thou perhaps mayst move
> That heart, which now abhors, to like his love.

> *(Exeunt.)*

THE MERCHANT OF VENICE

Act 4, Scene 1
3 Characters: 2 male, 1 female
Bassanio (M), Antonio (M), Portia (F)

After having saved Antonio from Shylock's revenge, Portia (disguised as a lawyer), demands a fee from Bassanio — the ring that she (as Portia) gave to him in Act 3. Bassanio refuses at first, then upon Antonio's urging, relents.

———➤•◉•◀———

Venice. A court of justice.

BASSANIO

    Most worthy gentleman, I and my friend
    Have by your wisdom been this day acquitted
    Of grievous penalties; in lieu whereof,
    Three thousand ducats, due unto the Jew,
    We freely cope your courteous pains withal.

ANTONIO

    And stand indebted, over and above,
    In love and service to you evermore.

PORTIA

    He is well paid that is well satisfied;
    And I, delivering you, am satisfied
    And therein do account myself well paid:
    My mind was never yet more mercenary.
    I pray you, know me when we meet again:
    I wish you well, and so I take my leave.

BASSANIO

    Dear sir, of force I must attempt you further:

Take some remembrance of us, as a tribute,
Not as a fee: grant me two things, I pray you,
Not to deny me, and to pardon me.

PORTIA
You press me far, and therefore I will yield.

(To ANTONIO.)

Give me your gloves, I'll wear them for your sake;

(To BASSANIO.)

And, for your love, I'll take this ring from you:
Do not draw back your hand; I'll take no more;
And you in love shall not deny me this.

BASSANIO
This ring, good sir, alas, it is a trifle!
I will not shame myself to give you this.

PORTIA
I will have nothing else but only this;
And now methinks I have a mind to it.

BASSANIO
There's more depends on this than on the value.
The dearest ring in Venice will I give you,
And find it out by proclamation:
Only for this, I pray you, pardon me.

PORTIA
I see, sir, you are liberal in offers
You taught me first to beg; and now methinks
You teach me how a beggar should be answer'd.

BASSANIO

 Good sir, this ring was given me by my wife;
 And when she put it on, she made me vow
 That I should neither sell nor give nor lose it.

PORTIA

 That 'scuse serves many men to save their gifts.
 An if your wife be not a mad-woman,
 And know how well I have deserved the ring,
 She would not hold out enemy for ever,
 For giving it to me. Well, peace be with you!

 (Exeunt PORTIA.)

ANTONIO

 My Lord Bassanio, let him have the ring:
 Let his deservings and my love withal
 Be valued against your wife's commandment.

BASSANIO

 Go, Gratiano, run and overtake him;
 Give him the ring, and bring him, if thou canst,
 Unto Antonio's house: away! make haste.
 Come, you and I will thither presently;
 And in the morning early will we both
 Fly toward Belmont: come, Antonio.

 (Exeunt.)

THE TEMPEST

Act 3, Scene 1
3 Characters: 2 male, 1 female
Ferdinand (M), Prospero (M), Miranda (F)

Ferdinand and Miranda reveal their love for each other. They are overheard by Miranda's father, Prospero, who is pleased his plan for them to come together has succeeded.

⟹●⟸

Before Prospero's cell. Enter FERDINAND, bearing a log.

FERDINAND

    There be some sports are painful, and their labour
    Delight in them sets off: some kinds of baseness
    Are nobly undergone and most poor matters
    Point to rich ends. This my mean task
    Would be as heavy to me as odious, but
    The mistress which I serve quickens what's dead
    And makes my labours pleasures: O, she is
    Ten times more gentle than her father's crabbed,
    And he's composed of harshness. I must remove
    Some thousands of these logs and pile them up,
    Upon a sore injunction: my sweet mistress
    Weeps when she sees me work, and says, such baseness
    Had never like executor. I forget:
    But these sweet thoughts do even refresh my labours,
    Most busy lest, when I do it.

(Enter MIRANDA; and PROSPERO at a distance, unseen.)

MIRANDA

    Alas, now, pray you,
    Work not so hard: I would the lightning had

Burnt up those logs that you are enjoin'd to pile!
Pray, set it down and rest you: when this burns,
'Twill weep for having wearied you. My father
Is hard at study; pray now, rest yourself;
He's safe for these three hours.

FERDINAND

O most dear mistress,
The sun will set before I shall discharge
What I must strive to do.

MIRANDA

If you'll sit down,
I'll bear your logs the while: pray, give me that;
I'll carry it to the pile.

FERDINAND

No, precious creature;
I had rather crack my sinews, break my back,
Than you should such dishonour undergo,
While I sit lazy by.

MIRANDA

It would become me
As well as it does you: and I should do it
With much more ease; for my good will is to it,
And yours it is against.

PROSPERO

Poor worm, thou art infected!
This visitation shows it.

MIRANDA

You look wearily.

FERDINAND

No, noble mistress; 'tis fresh morning with me

When you are by at night. I do beseech you —
Chiefly that I might set it in my prayers —
What is your name?

MIRANDA
Miranda. — O my father,
I have broke your hest to say so!

FERDINAND
Admired Miranda!
Indeed the top of admiration! worth
What's dearest to the world! Full many a lady
I have eyed with best regard and many a time
The harmony of their tongues hath into bondage
Brought my too diligent ear: for several virtues
Have I liked several women; never any
With so fun soul, but some defect in her
Did quarrel with the noblest grace she owed
And put it to the foil: but you, O you,
So perfect and so peerless, are created
Of every creature's best!

MIRANDA
I do not know
One of my sex; no woman's face remember,
Save, from my glass, mine own; nor have I seen
More that I may call men than you, good friend,
And my dear father: how features are abroad,
I am skilless of; but, by my modesty,
The jewel in my dower, I would not wish
Any companion in the world but you,
Nor can imagination form a shape,
Besides yourself, to like of. But I prattle
Something too wildly and my father's precepts
I therein do forget.

FERDINAND

    I am in my condition
    A prince, Miranda; I do think, a king;
    I would, not so! — and would no more endure
    This wooden slavery than to suffer
    The flesh-fly blow my mouth. Hear my soul speak:
    The very instant that I saw you, did
    My heart fly to your service; there resides,
    To make me slave to it; and for your sake
    Am I this patient log — man.

MIRANDA

    Do you love me?

FERDINAND

    O heaven, O earth, bear witness to this sound
    And crown what I profess with kind event
    If I speak true! if hollowly, invert
    What best is boded me to mischief! I
    Beyond all limit of what else i' the world
    Do love, prize, honour you.

MIRANDA

    I am a fool
    To weep at what I am glad of.

PROSPERO

    Fair encounter
    Of two most rare affections! Heavens rain grace
    On that which breeds between 'em!

FERDINAND

    Wherefore weep you?

MIRANDA

    At mine unworthiness that dare not offer

What I desire to give, and much less take
What I shall die to want. But this is trifling;
And all the more it seeks to hide itself,
The bigger bulk it shows. Hence, bashful cunning!
And prompt me, plain and holy innocence!
I am your wife, it you will marry me;
If not, I'll die your maid: to be your fellow
You may deny me; but I'll be your servant,
Whether you will or no.

FERDINAND

My mistress, dearest;
And I thus humble ever.

MIRANDA

My husband, then?

FERDINAND

Ay, with a heart as willing
As bondage e'er of freedom: here's my hand.

MIRANDA

And mine, with my heart in't; and now farewell
Till half an hour hence.

FERDINAND

A thousand thousand!

(Exeunt FERDINAND and MIRANDA severally.)

PROSPERO

So glad of this as they I cannot be,
Who are surprised withal; but my rejoicing
At nothing can be more. I'll to my book,
For yet ere supper-time must I perform
Much business appertaining.

(Exit.)

HAMLET

Act 2, Scene 2
3 Characters: 3 male
Hamlet, Polonius, First Player

A group of Players (actors) have arrived at Elsinore, and Hamlet greets them enthusiastically, reciting a scene from the Trojan War epic, Virgil's *Aeneid*. This scene recounts King Priam's murder by Pyrrhus and climaxes in a description of Hecuba, Priam's wife, grieving for her husband — giving Hamlet the idea to create a short play that would get Claudius to admit his killing of Hamlet's father.

⟫•◦•⟪

A room in the castle.

HAMLET
    Why,
    'As by lot, God wot,'
    and then, you know,
    'It came to pass, as most like it was,' —
    the first row of the pious chanson will show you
    more; for look, where my abridgement comes.
    You are welcome, masters; welcome, all. I am glad
    to see thee well. Welcome, good friends. O, my old
    friend! thy face is valenced since I saw thee last:
    comest thou to beard me in Denmark? What, my young
    lady and mistress! By'r lady, your ladyship is
    nearer to heaven than when I saw you last, by the
    altitude of a chopine. Pray God, your voice, like
    a piece of uncurrent gold, be not cracked within the
    ring. Masters, you are all welcome. We'll e'en
    to't like French falconers, fly at any thing we see:
    we'll have a speech straight: come, give us a taste
    of your quality; come, a passionate speech.

FIRST PLAYER
    What speech, my lord?

HAMLET
    I heard thee speak me a speech once, but it was
    never acted; or, if it was, not above once; for the
    play, I remember, pleased not the million; 'twas
    caviare to the general: but it was — as I received
    it, and others, whose judgments in such matters
    cried in the top of mine — an excellent play, well
    digested in the scenes, set down with as much
    modesty as cunning. I remember, one said there
    were no sallets in the lines to make the matter
    savoury, nor no matter in the phrase that might
    indict the author of affectation; but called it an
    honest method, as wholesome as sweet, and by very
    much more handsome than fine. One speech in it I
    chiefly loved: 'twas Aeneas' tale to Dido; and
    thereabout of it especially, where he speaks of
    Priam's slaughter: if it live in your memory, begin
    at this line: let me see, let me see —
    'The rugged Pyrrhus, like the Hyrcanian beast,' —
    it is not so: — it begins with Pyrrhus: —
    'The rugged Pyrrhus, he whose sable arms,
    Black as his purpose, did the night resemble
    When he lay couched in the ominous horse,
    Hath now this dread and black complexion smear'd
    With heraldry more dismal; head to foot
    Now is he total gules; horridly trick'd
    With blood of fathers, mothers, daughters, sons,
    Baked and impasted with the parching streets,
    That lend a tyrannous and damned light
    To their lord's murder: roasted in wrath and fire,
    And thus o'er-sized with coagulate gore,
    With eyes like carbuncles, the hellish Pyrrhus
    Old grandsire Priam seeks.'
    So, proceed you.

LORD POLONIUS
>'Fore God, my lord, well spoken, with good accent and good discretion.

FIRST PLAYER
>'Anon he finds him
>Striking too short at Greeks; his antique sword,
>Rebellious to his arm, lies where it falls,
>Repugnant to command: unequal match'd,
>Pyrrhus at Priam drives; in rage strikes wide;
>But with the whiff and wind of his fell sword
>The unnerved father falls. Then senseless Ilium,
>Seeming to feel this blow, with flaming top
>Stoops to his base, and with a hideous crash
>Takes prisoner Pyrrhus's ear: for, lo! his sword,
>Which was declining on the milky head
>Of reverend Priam, seem'd i' the air to stick:
>So, as a painted tyrant, Pyrrhus stood,
>And like a neutral to his will and matter,
>Did nothing.
>But, as we often see, against some storm,
>A silence in the heavens, the rack stand still,
>The bold winds speechless and the orb below
>As hush as death, anon the dreadful thunder
>Doth rend the region, so, after Pyrrhus's pause,
>Aroused vengeance sets him new a-work;
>And never did the Cyclops's hammers fall
>On Mars's armour forged for proof eterne
>With less remorse than Pyrrhus's bleeding sword
>Now falls on Priam.
>Out, out, thou strumpet, Fortune! All you gods,
>In general synod 'take away her power;
>Break all the spokes and fellies from her wheel,
>And bowl the round nave down the hill of heaven,
>As low as to the fiends!'

LORD POLONIUS

    This is too long.

HAMLET

    It shall to the barber's, with your beard. Prithee,
    say on: he's for a jig or a tale of bawdry, or he
    sleeps: say on: come to Hecuba.

FIRST PLAYER

    'But who, O, who had seen the mobled queen — '

HAMLET

    'The mobled queen?'

LORD POLONIUS

    That's good; 'mobled queen' is good.

FIRST PLAYER

    'Run barefoot up and down, threatening the flames
    With bisson rheum; a clout upon that head
    Where late the diadem stood, and for a robe,
    About her lank and all o'er-teemed loins,
    A blanket, in the alarm of fear caught up;
    Who this had seen, with tongue in venom steep'd,
    'Gainst Fortune's state would treason have
    pronounced:
    But if the gods themselves did see her then
    When she saw Pyrrhus make malicious sport
    In mincing with his sword her husband's limbs,
    The instant burst of clamour that she made,
    Unless things mortal move them not at all,
    Would have made milch the burning eyes of heaven,
    And passion in the gods.'

LORD POLONIUS

    Look, whether he has not turned his colour and has
    tears in's eyes. Pray you, no more.

HAMLET

    'Tis well: I'll have thee speak out the rest soon.
    Good my lord, will you see the players well
    bestowed? Do you hear, let them be well used; for
    they are the abstract and brief chronicles of the
    time: after your death you were better have a bad
    epitaph than their ill report while you live.

LORD POLONIUS

    My lord, I will use them according to their desert.

HAMLET

    God's bodykins, man, much better: use every man
    after his desert, and who should 'scape whipping?
    Use them after your own honour and dignity: the less
    they deserve, the more merit is in your bounty.
    Take them in.

LORD POLONIUS

    Come, sirs.

HAMLET

    Follow him, friends: we'll hear a play to-morrow.

JULIUS CAESAR

Act 4, Scene 3
3 Characters: 3 male
Ghost of Caesar, Brutus, Lucius

After assassinating Caesar, Brutus sees the Ghost of Caesar, which prophesies that, as punishment for the murder, Brutus will not survive the next day's battle.

➤◦◄

Brutus's tent.

BRUTUS
> It was well done; and thou shalt sleep again;
> I will not hold thee long: if I do live,
> I will be good to thee.

(Music, and a song.)

> This is a sleepy tune. O murderous slumber,
> Lay'st thou thy leaden mace upon my boy,
> That plays thee music? Gentle knave, good night;
> I will not do thee so much wrong to wake thee:
> If thou dost nod, thou break'st thy instrument;
> I'll take it from thee; and, good boy, good night.
> Let me see, let me see; is not the leaf turn'd down
> Where I left reading? Here it is, I think.

(Enter the GHOST of Caesar.)

> How ill this taper burns! Ha! who comes here?
> I think it is the weakness of mine eyes
> That shapes this monstrous apparition.
> It comes upon me. Art thou any thing?

Art thou some god, some angel, or some devil,
That makest my blood cold and my hair to stare?
Speak to me what thou art.

GHOST

Thy evil spirit, Brutus.

BRUTUS

Why comest thou?

GHOST

To tell thee thou shalt see me at Philippi.

BRUTUS

Well; then I shall see thee again?

GHOST

Ay, at Philippi.

BRUTUS

Why, I will see thee at Philippi, then.

(Exit GHOST.)

Now I have taken heart thou vanishest:
Ill spirit, I would hold more talk with thee.
Boy, Lucius! Varro! Claudius! Sirs, awake! Claudius!

LUCIUS

The strings, my lord, are false.

BRUTUS

He thinks he still is at his instrument.
Lucius, awake!

LUCIUS

My lord?

BRUTUS

Didst thou dream, Lucius, that thou so criedst out?

LUCIUS

My lord, I do not know that I did cry.

BRUTUS

Yes, that thou didst: didst thou see any thing?

LUCIUS

Nothing, my lord.

BRUTUS

Sleep again, Lucius. Sirrah Claudius!

SCENES FOR
FOUR CHARACTERS

THE MERRY WIVES OF WINDSOR

Act 4, Scene 1

4 Characters: 2 female, 2 male

Mistress Page (F), Mistress Quickly (F), William Page (M), Sir Hugh Evans (M)

This is a comic interlude with Mistress Page and the town matchmaker, Mistress Quickly, commenting upon the Latin lesson given by the parson, Sir Hugh Evans, to Mistress Page's son, William.

⟹•◦•⟸

A street. Enter MISTRESS PAGE, MISTRESS QUICKLY, and WILLIAM PAGE.

MISTRESS PAGE

Is he at Master Ford's already, think'st thou?

MISTRESS QUICKLY

Sure he is by this, or will be presently: but,
truly, he is very courageous mad about his throwing
into the water. Mistress Ford desires you to come suddenly.

MISTRESS PAGE

I'll be with her by and by; I'll but bring my young
man here to school. Look, where his master comes;
'tis a playing-day, I see.

(Enter SIR HUGH EVANS.)

How now, Sir Hugh! no school to-day?

SIR HUGH EVANS

No; Master Slender is let the boys leave to play.

MISTRESS QUICKLY

Blessing of his heart!

MISTRESS PAGE

Sir Hugh, my husband says my son profits nothing in
the world at his book. I pray you, ask him some
questions in his accidence.

SIR HUGH EVANS

Come hither, William; hold up your head; come.

MISTRESS PAGE

Come on, sirrah; hold up your head; answer your
master, be not afraid.

SIR HUGH EVANS

William, how many numbers is in nouns?

WILLIAM PAGE

Two.

MISTRESS QUICKLY

Truly, I thought there had been one number more,
because they say, ''Od's nouns.'

SIR HUGH EVANS

Peace your tattlings! What is 'fair,' William?

WILLIAM PAGE

Pulcher.

MISTRESS QUICKLY

Polecats! there are fairer things than polecats, sure.

SIR HUGH EVANS

You are a very simplicity 'oman: I pray you peace.
What is 'lapis,' William?

WILLIAM PAGE

A stone.

SIR HUGH EVANS
    And what is 'a stone,' William?

WILLIAM PAGE
    A pebble.

SIR HUGH EVANS
    No, it is 'lapis': I pray you, remember in your prain.

WILLIAM PAGE
    Lapis.

SIR HUGH EVANS
    That is a good William. What is he, William, that
    does lend articles?

WILLIAM PAGE
    Articles are borrowed of the pronoun, and be thus
    declined, Singulariter, nominativo, hic, haec, hoc.

SIR HUGH EVANS
    Nominativo, hig, hag, hog; pray you, mark:
    genitivo, hujus. Well, what is your accusative case?

WILLIAM PAGE
    Accusativo, hinc.

SIR HUGH EVANS
    I pray you, have your remembrance, child,
    accusative, hung, hang, hog.

MISTRESS QUICKLY
    'Hang-hog' is Latin for bacon, I warrant you.

SIR HUGH EVANS
    Leave your prabbles, 'oman. What is the focative
    case, William?

WILLIAM PAGE

O, — vocativo, O.

SIR HUGH EVANS

Remember, William; focative is caret.

MISTRESS QUICKLY

And that's a good root.

SIR HUGH EVANS

'Oman, forbear.

MISTRESS PAGE

Peace!

SIR HUGH EVANS

What is your genitive case plural, William?

WILLIAM PAGE

Genitive case!

SIR HUGH EVANS

Ay.

WILLIAM PAGE

Genitive, — horum, harum, horum.

MISTRESS QUICKLY

Vengeance of Jenny's case! fie on her! never name
her, child, if she be a whore.

SIR HUGH EVANS

For shame, 'oman.

MISTRESS QUICKLY

You do ill to teach the child such words: he

teaches him to hick and to hack, which they'll do
fast enough of themselves, and to call 'horum': fie upon you!

SIR HUGH EVANS

'Oman, art thou lunatics? hast thou no
understandings for thy cases and the numbers of the
genders? Thou art as foolish Christian creatures as
I would desires.

MISTRESS PAGE

Prithee, hold thy peace.

SIR HUGH EVANS

Show me now, William, some declensions of your pronouns.

WILLIAM PAGE

Forsooth, I have forgot.

SIR HUGH EVANS

It is qui, quae, quod: if you forget your 'quies,'
your 'quaes,' and your 'quods,' you must be
preeches. Go your ways, and play; go.

MISTRESS PAGE

He is a better scholar than I thought he was.

SIR HUGH EVANS

He is a good sprag memory. Farewell, Mistress Page.

MISTRESS PAGE

Adieu, good Sir Hugh.

(*Exit SIR HUGH EVANS.*)

Get you home, boy. Come, we stay too long.

(*Exeunt.*)

TITUS ANDRONICUS

Act 5, Scene 3
4 Characters: 2 male, 2 female
Titus Andronicus (M), Saturninus (M), Lavinia (F), Tamora (F)

Earlier in this play, Tamora's sons, Demetrius and Chiron, had raped
Titus's daughter, Lavinia, and cut off her tongue and hands. Now,
before the banquet, Titus has killed Demetrius and Chiron and
ground their body and blood into pies, which he plans to serve to
their mother.

━━━━➤●◀━━━━

Court of Titus's house. A banquet set out. Hautboys sound.
The company sit down at table. Enter TITUS dressed like a
cook, LAVINIA veiled, TAMORA, and SATURNINUS.
TITUS places the dishes on the table.

TITUS ANDRONICUS
    Welcome, my gracious lord; welcome, dread queen;
    Welcome, ye warlike Goths; welcome, Lucius;
    And welcome, all: although the cheer be poor,
    'Twill fill your stomachs; please you eat of it.

SATURNINUS
    Why art thou thus attired, Andronicus?

TITUS ANDRONICUS
    Because I would be sure to have all well,
    To entertain your highness and your empress.

TAMORA
    We are beholding to you, good Andronicus.

TITUS ANDRONICUS
An if your highness knew my heart, you were.
My lord the emperor, resolve me this:
Was it well done of rash Virginius
To slay his daughter with his own right hand,
Because she was enforced, stain'd, and deflower'd?

SATURNINUS
It was, Andronicus.

TITUS ANDRONICUS
Your reason, mighty lord?

SATURNINUS
Because the girl should not survive her shame,
And by her presence still renew his sorrows.

TITUS ANDRONICUS
A reason mighty, strong, and effectual;
A pattern, precedent, and lively warrant,
For me, most wretched, to perform the like.
Die, die, Lavinia, and thy shame with thee;

(Kills LAVINIA.)

And, with thy shame, thy father's sorrow die!

SATURNINUS
What hast thou done, unnatural and unkind?

TITUS ANDRONICUS
Kill'd her, for whom my tears have made me blind.
I am as woeful as Virginius was,
And have a thousand times more cause than he
To do this outrage: and it now is done.

SATURNINUS

What, was she ravish'd? tell who did the deed.

TITUS ANDRONICUS

Will't please you eat? will't please your
highness feed?

TAMORA

Why hast thou slain thine only daughter thus?

TITUS ANDRONICUS

Not I; 'twas Chiron and Demetrius:
They ravish'd her, and cut away her tongue;
And they, 'twas they, that did her all this wrong.

SATURNINUS

Go fetch them hither to us presently.

TITUS ANDRONICUS

Why, there they are both, baked in that pie;
Whereof their mother daintily hath fed,
Eating the flesh that she herself hath bred.
'Tis true, 'tis true; witness my knife's sharp point.

(Kills TAMORA.)

SATURNINUS

Die, frantic wretch, for this accursed deed!

(Kills TITUS.)

MEASURE FOR MEASURE

Act 2, Scene 2

4 Characters: 3 male, 1 female

Angelo (M), Lucio (M), Provost (M), Isabella (F)

With her friend, Lucio, giving advice, Isabella begs Angelo to stay her brother's execution.

—————⊷•⊶—————

Another room in Angelo's house.

ISABELLA

    I am a woeful suitor to your honour,

    Please but your honour hear me.

ANGELO

    Well; what's your suit?

ISABELLA

    There is a vice that most I do abhor,

    And most desire should meet the blow of justice;

    For which I would not plead, but that I must;

    For which I must not plead, but that I am

    At war 'twixt will and will not.

ANGELO

    Well; the matter?

ISABELLA

    I have a brother is condemn'd to die:

    I do beseech you, let it be his fault,

    And not my brother.

PROVOST

    (Aside.) Heaven give thee moving graces!

ANGELO

    Condemn the fault and not the actor of it?
    Why, every fault's condemn'd ere it be done:
    Mine were the very cipher of a function,
    To fine the faults whose fine stands in record,
    And let go by the actor.

ISABELLA

    O just but severe law!
    I had a brother, then. Heaven keep your honour!

LUCIO

    (Aside to ISABELLA.) Give't not o'er so: to him
    again, entreat him;
    Kneel down before him, hang upon his gown:
    You are too cold; if you should need a pin,
    You could not with more tame a tongue desire it:
    To him, I say!

ISABELLA

    Must he needs die?

ANGELO

    Maiden, no remedy.

ISABELLA

    Yes; I do think that you might pardon him,
    And neither heaven nor man grieve at the mercy.

ANGELO

    I will not do't.

ISABELLA

    But can you, if you would?

ANGELO

Look, what I will not, that I cannot do.

ISABELLA

But might you do't, and do the world no wrong,
If so your heart were touch'd with that remorse
As mine is to him?

ANGELO

He's sentenced; 'tis too late.

LUCIO

(Aside to ISABELLA.) You are too cold.

ISABELLA

Too late? why, no; I, that do speak a word.
May call it back again. Well, believe this,
No ceremony that to great ones 'longs,
Not the king's crown, nor the deputed sword,
The marshal's truncheon, nor the judge's robe,
Become them with one half so good a grace
As mercy does.
If he had been as you and you as he,
You would have slipt like him; but he, like you,
Would not have been so stern.

ANGELO

Pray you, be gone.

ISABELLA

I would to heaven I had your potency,
And you were Isabel! should it then be thus?
No; I would tell what 'twere to be a judge,
And what a prisoner.

LUCIO

    (Aside to ISABELLA.) Ay, touch him; there's the vein.

ANGELO

    Your brother is a forfeit of the law,
    And you but waste your words.

ISABELLA

    Alas, alas!
    Why, all the souls that were were forfeit once;
    And He that might the vantage best have took
    Found out the remedy. How would you be,
    If He, which is the top of judgment, should
    But judge you as you are? O, think on that;
    And mercy then will breathe within your lips,
    Like man new made.

ANGELO

    Be you content, fair maid;
    It is the law, not I condemn your brother:
    Were he my kinsman, brother, or my son,
    It should be thus with him: he must die tomorrow.

ISABELLA

    To-morrow! O, that's sudden! Spare him, spare him!
    He's not prepared for death. Even for our kitchens
    We kill the fowl of season: shall we serve heaven
    With less respect than we do minister
    To our gross selves? Good, good my lord, bethink you;
    Who is it that hath died for this offence?
    There's many have committed it.

LUCIO

    (Aside to ISABELLA.) Ay, well said.

ANGELO

    The law hath not been dead, though it hath slept:

Those many had not dared to do that evil,
If the first that did the edict infringe
Had answer'd for his deed: now 'tis awake
Takes note of what is done; and, like a prophet,
Looks in a glass, that shows what future evils,
Either new, or by remissness new-conceived,
And so in progress to be hatch'd and born,
Are now to have no successive degrees,
But, ere they live, to end.

ISABELLA

Yet show some pity.

ANGELO

I show it most of all when I show justice;
For then I pity those I do not know,
Which a dismiss'd offence would after gall;
And do him right that, answering one foul wrong,
Lives not to act another. Be satisfied;
Your brother dies to-morrow; be content.

ISABELLA

So you must be the first that gives this sentence,
And he, that suffers. O, it is excellent
To have a giant's strength; but it is tyrannous
To use it like a giant.

MUCH ADO ABOUT NOTHING

Act 2, Scene 1
4 Characters: 3 male, 1 female
Leonato (M), Antonio (M), Hero (M), Beatrice (F)

As Beatrice makes a sarcastic comparison between the quiet Don John and the talkative Benedick, her uncle Leonato upbraids her negative views concerning men and marriage, predicting she will die an old maid.

———⟫•◦•⟪———

A hall in Leonato's house. Enter LEONATO, ANTONIO, HERO, BEATRICE, and others.

LEONATO
  Was not Count John here at supper?

ANTONIO
  I saw him not.

BEATRICE
  How tartly that gentleman looks! I never can see
  him but I am heart-burned an hour after.

HERO
  He is of a very melancholy disposition.

BEATRICE
  He were an excellent man that were made just in the
  midway between him and Benedick: the one is too
  like an image and says nothing, and the other too
  like my lady's eldest son, evermore tattling.

LEONATO
  Then half Signior Benedick's tongue in Count John's

mouth, and half Count John's melancholy in Signior
Benedick's face, —

BEATRICE

With a good leg and a good foot, uncle, and money
enough in his purse, such a man would win any woman
in the world, if a' could get her good-will.

LEONATO

By my troth, niece, thou wilt never get thee a
husband, if thou be so shrewd of thy tongue.

ANTONIO

In faith, she's too curst.

BEATRICE

Too curst is more than curst: I shall lessen God's
sending that way; for it is said, 'God sends a curst
cow short horns;' but to a cow too curst he sends none.

LEONATO

So, by being too curst, God will send you no horns.

BEATRICE

Just, if he send me no husband; for the which
blessing I am at him upon my knees every morning and
evening. Lord, I could not endure a husband with a
beard on his face: I had rather lie in the woollen.

LEONATO

You may light on a husband that hath no beard.

BEATRICE

What should I do with him? dress him in my apparel
and make him my waiting-gentlewoman? He that hath a
beard is more than a youth, and he that hath no

beard is less than a man: and he that is more than
a youth is not for me, and he that is less than a
man, I am not for him: therefore, I will even take
sixpence in earnest of the bear-ward, and lead his
apes into hell.

LEONATO
Well, then, go you into hell?

BEATRICE
No, but to the gate; and there will the devil meet
me, like an old cuckold, with horns on his head, and
say 'Get you to heaven, Beatrice, get you to
heaven; here's no place for you maids:' so deliver
I up my apes, and away to Saint Peter for the
heavens; he shows me where the bachelors sit, and
there live we as merry as the day is long.

ANTONIO
(To HERO.) Well, niece, I trust you will be ruled
by your father.

BEATRICE
Yes, faith; it is my cousin's duty to make curtsy
and say 'Father, as it please you.' But yet for all
that, cousin, let him be a handsome fellow, or else
make another curtsy and say 'Father, as it please
me.'

LEONATO
Well, niece, I hope to see you one day fitted with a husband.

BEATRICE
Not till God make men of some other metal than
earth. Would it not grieve a woman to be
overmastered with a piece of valiant dust? to make

an account of her life to a clod of wayward marl?
No, uncle, I'll none: Adam's sons are my brethren;
and, truly, I hold it a sin to match in my kindred.

LEONATO

Daughter, remember what I told you: if the prince
do solicit you in that kind, you know your answer.

BEATRICE

The fault will be in the music, cousin, if you be
not wooed in good time: if the prince be too
important, tell him there is measure in every thing
and so dance out the answer. For, hear me, Hero:
wooing, wedding, and repenting, is as a Scotch jig,
a measure, and a cinque pace: the first suit is hot
and hasty, like a Scotch jig, and full as
fantastical; the wedding, mannerly-modest, as a
measure, full of state and ancientry; and then comes
repentance and, with his bad legs, falls into the
cinque pace faster and faster, till he sink into his grave.

LEONATO

Cousin, you apprehend passing shrewdly.

BEATRICE

I have a good eye, uncle; I can see a church by daylight.

LEONATO

The revellers are entering, brother: make good room.

THE MERCHANT OF VENICE

Act 5, Scene 1
4 Characters: 3 male, 1 female
Lorenzo (M), Stephano (M), Launcelot (M), Jessica (F)

In the final scene of the play, Lorenzo and Jessica revel in their love
and welcome the announcements of pending arrivals by Portia and
Bassanio.

------→◦←------

*Belmont. Avenue to Portia's house. Enter LORENZO and
JESSICA.*

LORENZO
    The moon shines bright: in such a night as this,
    When the sweet wind did gently kiss the trees
    And they did make no noise, in such a night
    Troilus methinks mounted the Troyan walls
    And sigh'd his soul toward the Grecian tents,
    Where Cressid lay that night.

JESSICA
    In such a night
    Did Thisbe fearfully o'ertrip the dew
    And saw the lion's shadow ere himself
    And ran dismay'd away.

LORENZO
    In such a night
    Stood Dido with a willow in her hand
    Upon the wild sea banks and waft her love
    To come again to Carthage.

JESSICA
    In such a night

Medea gather'd the enchanted herbs
That did renew old AEson.

LORENZO
In such a night
Did Jessica steal from the wealthy Jew
And with an unthrift love did run from Venice
As far as Belmont.

JESSICA
In such a night
Did young Lorenzo swear he loved her well,
Stealing her soul with many vows of faith
And ne'er a true one.

LORENZO
In such a night
Did pretty Jessica, like a little shrew,
Slander her love, and he forgave it her.

JESSICA
I would out-night you, did no body come;
But, hark, I hear the footing of a man.

(Enter STEPHANO.)

LORENZO
Who comes so fast in silence of the night?

STEPHANO
A friend.

LORENZO
A friend! what friend? your name, I pray you, friend?

STEPHANO
Stephano is my name; and I bring word

My mistress will before the break of day
Be here at Belmont; she doth stray about
By holy crosses, where she kneels and prays
For happy wedlock hours.

LORENZO
Who comes with her?

STEPHANO
None but a holy hermit and her maid.
I pray you, is my master yet return'd?

LORENZO
He is not, nor we have not heard from him.
But go we in, I pray thee, Jessica,
And ceremoniously let us prepare
Some welcome for the mistress of the house.

(Enter LAUNCELOT.)

LAUNCELOT
Sola, sola! wo ha, ho! sola, sola!

LORENZO
Who calls?

LAUNCELOT
Sola! did you see Master Lorenzo?
Master Lorenzo, sola, sola!

LORENZO
Leave hollaing, man: here.

LAUNCELOT
Sola! where? where?

LORENZO

Here.

LAUNCELOT

Tell him there's a post come from my master, with
his horn full of good news: my master will be here
ere morning.

(Exit.)

LORENZO

Sweet soul, let's in, and there expect their coming.
And yet no matter: why should we go in?
My friend Stephano, signify, I pray you,
Within the house, your mistress is at hand;
And bring your music forth into the air.

(Exit STEPHANO.)

How sweet the moonlight sleeps upon this bank!
Here will we sit and let the sounds of music
Creep in our ears: soft stillness and the night
Become the touches of sweet harmony.
Sit, Jessica. Look how the floor of heaven
Is thick inlaid with patines of bright gold:
There's not the smallest orb which thou behold'st
But in his motion like an angel sings,
Still quiring to the young-eyed cherubins;
Such harmony is in immortal souls;
But whilst this muddy vesture of decay
Doth grossly close it in, we cannot hear it.

KING LEAR

Act 1, Scene 1
4 Characters: 3 female, 1 male
Goneril (F), Regan (F), Cordelia (F), King Lear (M)

Elderly King Lear has decided he will divide the kingdom among his three daughters, giving the biggest share to the daughter who loves him the most. The evil Goneril and Regan offer insincere declarations of affection, but Cordelia — who truly loves her father — says only that she loves him as always. Lear is enraged and disowns Cordelia.

———➤●◀———

King Lear's palace.

KING LEAR
    Meantime we shall express our darker purpose.
    Give me the map there. Know that we have divided
    In three our kingdom: and 'tis our fast intent
    To shake all cares and business from our age;
    Conferring them on younger strengths, while we
    Unburthen'd crawl toward death. Our son of Cornwall,
    And you, our no less loving son of Albany,
    We have this hour a constant will to publish
    Our daughters' several dowers, that future strife
    May be prevented now. The princes, France and Burgundy,
    Great rivals in our youngest daughter's love,
    Long in our court have made their amorous sojourn,
    And here are to be answer'd. Tell me, my daughters, —
    Since now we will divest us both of rule,
    Interest of territory, cares of state, —
    Which of you shall we say doth love us most?
    That we our largest bounty may extend
    Where nature doth with merit challenge. Goneril,
    Our eldest-born, speak first.

GONERIL

> Sir, I love you more than words can wield the matter;
> Dearer than eye-sight, space, and liberty;
> Beyond what can be valued, rich or rare;
> No less than life, with grace, health, beauty, honour;
> As much as child e'er loved, or father found;
> A love that makes breath poor, and speech unable;
> Beyond all manner of so much I love you.

CORDELIA

> *(Aside.)* What shall Cordelia do?
> Love, and be silent.

LEAR

> Of all these bounds, even from this line to this,
> With shadowy forests and with champains rich'd,
> With plenteous rivers and wide-skirted meads,
> We make thee lady: to thine and Albany's issue
> Be this perpetual. What says our second daughter,
> Our dearest Regan, wife to Cornwall? Speak.

REGAN

> Sir, I am made
> Of the self-same metal that my sister is,
> And prize me at her worth. In my true heart
> I find she names my very deed of love;
> Only she comes too short: that I profess
> Myself an enemy to all other joys,
> Which the most precious square of sense possesses;
> And find I am alone felicitate
> In your dear highness' love.

CORDELIA

> *(Aside.)* Then poor Cordelia!
> And yet not so; since, I am sure, my love's
> More richer than my tongue.

KING LEAR

    To thee and thine hereditary ever
    Remain this ample third of our fair kingdom;
    No less in space, validity, and pleasure,
    Than that conferr'd on Goneril. Now, our joy,
    Although the last, not least; to whose young love
    The vines of France and milk of Burgundy
    Strive to be interess'd; what can you say to draw
    A third more opulent than your sisters? Speak.

CORDELIA

    Nothing, my lord.

KING LEAR

    Nothing!

CORDELIA

    Nothing.

KING LEAR

    Nothing will come of nothing: speak again.

CORDELIA

    Unhappy that I am, I cannot heave
    My heart into my mouth: I love your majesty
    According to my bond; nor more nor less.

KING LEAR

    How, how, Cordelia! mend your speech a little,
    Lest it may mar your fortunes.

CORDELIA

    Good my lord,
    You have begot me, bred me, loved me: I
    Return those duties back as are right fit,
    Obey you, love you, and most honour you.

Why have my sisters husbands, if they say
They love you all? Haply, when I shall wed,
That lord whose hand must take my plight shall carry
Half my love with him, half my care and duty:
Sure, I shall never marry like my sisters,
To love my father all.

KING LEAR

But goes thy heart with this?

CORDELIA

Ay, good my lord.

KING LEAR

So young, and so untender?

CORDELIA

So young, my lord, and true.

KING LEAR

Let it be so; thy truth, then, be thy dower:
For, by the sacred radiance of the sun,
The mysteries of Hecate, and the night;
By all the operation of the orbs
From whom we do exist, and cease to be;
Here I disclaim all my paternal care,
Propinquity and property of blood,
And as a stranger to my heart and me
Hold thee, from this, for ever. The barbarous Scythian,
Or he that makes his generation messes
To gorge his appetite, shall to my bosom
Be as well neighbour'd, pitied, and relieved,
As thou my sometime daughter.

MUCH ADO ABOUT NOTHING

Act 3, Scene 1
4 Characters: 3 female, 1 male
Margaret (F), Ursula (F), Beatrice (F), Hero (M)

Hero and Ursula tell Margaret to lure Beatrice into the garden by making her believe she can eavesdrop on them. As Beatrice hides, Hero and Ursula discuss Benedick and his love for Beatrice. The trick works, and Beatrice vows to marry Benedick.

————◆————

Leonato's garden. Enter HERO, MARGARET, and URSULA.

HERO

    Good Margaret, run thee to the parlor;
    There shalt thou find my cousin Beatrice
    Proposing with the prince and Claudio:
    Whisper her ear and tell her, I and Ursula
    Walk in the orchard and our whole discourse
    Is all of her; say that thou overheard'st us;
    And bid her steal into the pleached bower,
    Where honeysuckles, ripen'd by the sun,
    Forbid the sun to enter, like favourites,
    Made proud by princes, that advance their pride
    Against that power that bred it: there will she hide her,
    To listen our purpose. This is thy office;
    Bear thee well in it and leave us alone.

MARGARET

    I'll make her come, I warrant you, presently.

    (Exit.)

HERO

    Now, Ursula, when Beatrice doth come,

As we do trace this alley up and down,
Our talk must only be of Benedick.
When I do name him, let it be thy part
To praise him more than ever man did merit:
My talk to thee must be how Benedick
Is sick in love with Beatrice. Of this matter
Is little Cupid's crafty arrow made,
That only wounds by hearsay.

(Enter BEATRICE, behind.)

Now begin;
For look where Beatrice, like a lapwing, runs
Close by the ground, to hear our conference.

URSULA
The pleasant'st angling is to see the fish
Cut with her golden oars the silver stream,
And greedily devour the treacherous bait:
So angle we for Beatrice; who even now
Is couched in the woodbine coverture.
Fear you not my part of the dialogue.

HERO
Then go we near her, that her ear lose nothing
Of the false sweet bait that we lay for it.

(Approaching the bower.)

No, truly, Ursula, she is too disdainful;
I know her spirits are as coy and wild
As haggerds of the rock.

URSULA
But are you sure
That Benedick loves Beatrice so entirely?

HERO

So says the prince and my new-trothed lord.

URSULA

And did they bid you tell her of it, madam?

HERO

They did entreat me to acquaint her of it;
But I persuaded them, if they loved Benedick,
To wish him wrestle with affection,
And never to let Beatrice know of it.

URSULA

Why did you so? Doth not the gentleman
Deserve as full as fortunate a bed
As ever Beatrice shall couch upon?

HERO

O god of love! I know he doth deserve
As much as may be yielded to a man:
But Nature never framed a woman's heart
Of prouder stuff than that of Beatrice;
Disdain and scorn ride sparkling in her eyes,
Misprising what they look on, and her wit
Values itself so highly that to her
All matter else seems weak: she cannot love,
Nor take no shape nor project of affection,
She is so self-endeared.

URSULA

Sure, I think so;
And therefore certainly it were not good
She knew his love, lest she make sport at it.

HERO

Why, you speak truth. I never yet saw man,

How wise, how noble, young, how rarely featured,
But she would spell him backward: if fair-faced,
She would swear the gentleman should be her sister;
If black, why, Nature, drawing of an antique,
Made a foul blot; if tall, a lance ill-headed;
If low, an agate very vilely cut;
If speaking, why, a vane blown with all winds;
If silent, why, a block moved with none.
So turns she every man the wrong side out
And never gives to truth and virtue that
Which simpleness and merit purchaseth.

URSULA
Sure, sure, such carping is not commendable.

HERO
No, not to be so odd and from all fashions
As Beatrice is, cannot be commendable:
But who dare tell her so? If I should speak,
She would mock me into air; O, she would laugh me
Out of myself, press me to death with wit.
Therefore let Benedick, like cover'd fire,
Consume away in sighs, waste inwardly:
It were a better death than die with mocks,
Which is as bad as die with tickling.

URSULA
Yet tell her of it: hear what she will say.

HERO
No; rather I will go to Benedick
And counsel him to fight against his passion.
And, truly, I'll devise some honest slanders
To stain my cousin with: one doth not know
How much an ill word may empoison liking.

URSULA

O, do not do your cousin such a wrong.
She cannot be so much without true judgment —
Having so swift and excellent a wit
As she is prized to have — as to refuse
So rare a gentleman as Signior Benedick.

HERO

He is the only man of Italy.
Always excepted my dear Claudio.

URSULA

I pray you, be not angry with me, madam,
Speaking my fancy: Signior Benedick,
For shape, for bearing, argument and valour,
Goes foremost in report through Italy.

HERO

Indeed, he hath an excellent good name.

URSULA

His excellence did earn it, ere he had it.
When are you married, madam?

HERO

Why, every day, to-morrow. Come, go in:
I'll show thee some attires, and have thy counsel
Which is the best to furnish me to-morrow.

URSULA

She's limed, I warrant you: we have caught her, madam.

HERO

If it proves so, then loving goes by haps:
Some Cupid kills with arrows, some with traps.

(Exeunt HERO and URSULA.)

BEATRICE

(Coming forward.)

What fire is in mine ears? Can this be true?
Stand I condemn'd for pride and scorn so much?
Contempt, farewell! and maiden pride, adieu!
No glory lives behind the back of such.
And, Benedick, love on; I will requite thee,
Taming my wild heart to thy loving hand:
If thou dost love, my kindness shall incite thee
To bind our loves up in a holy band;
For others say thou dost deserve, and I
Believe it better than reportingly.

(Exit.)

MUCH ADO ABOUT NOTHING

Act 3, Scene 4
4 Characters: 3 female, 1 male
Margaret (F), Ursula (F), Beatrice (F), Hero (M)

Margaret and Ursula tease the newly love-struck Beatrice about her feelings for Benedick. Beatrice denies her behavior has changed because of love, claiming she simply has a cold.

—————➤●◄—————

Hero's apartment.

HERO
> Good morrow, coz.

BEATRICE
> Good morrow, sweet Hero.

HERO
> Why how now? do you speak in the sick tune?

BEATRICE
> I am out of all other tune, methinks.

MARGARET
> Clap's into 'Light o' love'; that goes without a
> burden: do you sing it, and I'll dance it.

BEATRICE
> Ye light o' love, with your heels! then, if your
> husband have stables enough, you'll see he shall
> lack no barns.

MARGARET
> O illegitimate construction! I scorn that with my heels.

BEATRICE
> 'Tis almost five o'clock, cousin; tis time you were
> ready. By my troth, I am exceeding ill: heigh-ho!

MARGARET
>For a hawk, a horse, or a husband?

BEATRICE
>For the letter that begins them all, H.

MARGARET
>Well, and you be not turned Turk, there's no more
>sailing by the star.

BEATRICE
>What means the fool, trow?

MARGARET
>Nothing I; but God send every one their heart's desire!

HERO
>These gloves the count sent me; they are an
>excellent perfume.

BEATRICE
>I am stuffed, cousin; I cannot smell.

MARGARET
>A maid, and stuffed! there's goodly catching of cold.

BEATRICE
>O, God help me! God help me! how long have you
>professed apprehension?

MARGARET
>Even since you left it. Doth not my wit become me rarely?

BEATRICE
>It is not seen enough, you should wear it in your
>cap. By my troth, I am sick.

MARGARET
>Get you some of this distilled Carduus Benedictus,
>and lay it to your heart: it is the only thing for a qualm.

HERO

There thou prickest her with a thistle.

BEATRICE

Benedictus! why Benedictus? you have some moral in this Benedictus.

MARGARET

Moral! no, by my troth, I have no moral meaning; I meant, plain holy-thistle. You may think perchance that I think you are in love: nay, by'r lady, I am not such a fool to think what I list, nor I list not to think what I can, nor indeed I cannot think, if I would think my heart out of thinking, that you are in love or that you will be in love or that you can be in love. Yet Benedick was such another, and now is he become a man: he swore he would never marry, and yet now, in despite of his heart, he eats his meat without grudging: and how you may be converted I know not, but methinks you look with your eyes as other women do.

BEATRICE

What pace is this that thy tongue keeps?

MARGARET

Not a false gallop.

(Re-enter URSULA.)

URSULA

Madam, withdraw: the prince, the count, Signior Benedick, Don John, and all the gallants of the town, are come to fetch you to church.

HERO

Help to dress me, good coz, good Meg, good Ursula.

(Exeunt.)

ALL'S WELL THAT ENDS WELL
Act 3, Scene 5
4 Characters: 4 female
Widow of Florence, Diana, Mariana, Helena

Helena arrives in Florence disguised as a pilgrim and meets the
Widow who has taken in Bertram, Helena's husband. Helena discovers that Bertram has been courting the Widow's daughter, Diana.

⟫—◦—⟪

*Florence. Without the walls. A tucket afar off. Enter an old
WIDOW OF FLORENCE, DIANA, and MARIANA, with
other CITIZENS.*

WIDOW
Nay, come; for if they do approach the city, we
shall lose all the sight.

DIANA
They say the French count has done most honourable service.

WIDOW
It is reported that he has taken their greatest
commander; and that with his own hand he slew the
duke's brother.

(Tucket.)

We have lost our labour; they are gone a contrary
way: hark! you may know by their trumpets.

MARIANA
Come, let's return again, and suffice ourselves with
the report of it. Well, Diana, take heed of this

French earl: the honour of a maid is her name; and
no legacy is so rich as honesty.

WIDOW

I have told my neighbour how you have been solicited
by a gentleman his companion.

MARIANA

I know that knave; hang him! one Parolles: a
filthy officer he is in those suggestions for the
young earl. Beware of them, Diana; their promises,
enticements, oaths, tokens, and all these engines of
lust, are not the things they go under: many a maid
hath been seduced by them; and the misery is,
example, that so terrible shows in the wreck of
maidenhood, cannot for all that dissuade succession,
but that they are limed with the twigs that threaten
them. I hope I need not to advise you further; but
I hope your own grace will keep you where you are,
though there were no further danger known but the
modesty which is so lost.

DIANA

You shall not need to fear me.

WIDOW

I hope so.

(Enter HELENA, disguised like a pilgrim.)

Look, here comes a pilgrim: I know she will lie at
my house; thither they send one another: I'll
question her. God save you, pilgrim! whither are you bound?

HELENA

To Saint Jaques le Grand.
Where do the palmers lodge, I do beseech you?

WIDOW

At the Saint Francis here beside the port.

HELENA

Is this the way?

WIDOW

Ay, marry, is't.

(A march afar.)

Hark you! they come this way.
If you will tarry, holy pilgrim,
But till the troops come by,
I will conduct you where you shall be lodged;
The rather, for I think I know your hostess
As ample as myself.

HELENA

Is it yourself?

WIDOW

If you shall please so, pilgrim.

HELENA

I thank you, and will stay upon your leisure.

WIDOW

You came, I think, from France?

HELENA

I did so.

WIDOW

Here you shall see a countryman of yours
That has done worthy service.

HELENA

>His name, I pray you.

DIANA

>The Count Rousillon: know you such a one?

HELENA

>But by the ear, that hears most nobly of him:
>His face I know not.

DIANA

>Whatsome'er he is,
>He's bravely taken here. He stole from France,
>As 'tis reported, for the king had married him
>Against his liking: think you it is so?

HELENA

>Ay, surely, mere the truth: I know his lady.

DIANA

>There is a gentleman that serves the count
>Reports but coarsely of her.

HELENA

>What's his name?

DIANA

>Monsieur Parolles.

HELENA

>O, I believe with him,
>In argument of praise, or to the worth
>Of the great count himself, she is too mean
>To have her name repeated: all her deserving
>Is a reserved honesty, and that
>I have not heard examined.

DIANA

Alas, poor lady!
'Tis a hard bondage to become the wife
Of a detesting lord.

WIDOW

I warrant, good creature, wheresoe'er she is,
Her heart weighs sadly: this young maid might do her
A shrewd turn, if she pleased.

HELENA

How do you mean?
May be the amorous count solicits her
In the unlawful purpose.

WIDOW

He does indeed;
And brokes with all that can in such a suit
Corrupt the tender honour of a maid:
But she is arm'd for him and keeps her guard
In honestest defence.

MARIANA

The gods forbid else!

WIDOW

So, now they come:

CORIOLANUS

Act 1, Scene 3
4 Characters: 4 female
Volumnia, Virgilia, Valeria, Gentlewoman

Marcius' mother, Volumnia, chastises his wife, Virgilia, for not rejoicing in her husband's departure for war. When Valeria, a friend of
Virgilia arrives, Volumnia refuses to let Virgilia leave before Volumnia expresses her bloody vision of Marcius on the battlefield smiting
his enemies. Virgilia is disgusted and vows not to leave her house
until her husband returns safely from war.

———➤●◄———

*Rome. A room in Marcius's house. Enter VOLUMNIA and
VIRGILIA. They sit down on two low stools and sew.*

VOLUMNIA

    I pray you, daughter, sing; or express yourself in a
    more comfortable sort: if my son were my husband, I
    should freelier rejoice in that absence wherein he
    won honour than in the embracements of his bed where
    he would show most love. When yet he was but
    tender-bodied and the only son of my womb, when
    youth with comeliness plucked all gaze his way, when
    for a day of kings' entreaties a mother should not
    sell him an hour from her beholding, I, considering
    how honour would become such a person. That it was
    no better than picture-like to hang by the wall, if
    renown made it not stir, was pleased to let him seek
    danger where he was like to find fame. To a cruel
    war I sent him; from whence he returned, his brows
    bound with oak. I tell thee, daughter, I sprang not
    more in joy at first hearing he was a man-child
    than now in first seeing he had proved himself a
    man.

VIRGILIA

But had he died in the business, madam; how then?

VOLUMNIA

Then his good report should have been my son; I
therein would have found issue. Hear me profess
sincerely: had I a dozen sons, each in my love
alike and none less dear than thine and my good
Marcius, I had rather had eleven die nobly for their
country than one voluptuously surfeit out of action.

(Enter a GENTLEWOMAN.)

GENTLEWOMAN

Madam, the Lady Valeria is come to visit you.

VIRGILIA

Beseech you, give me leave to retire myself.

VOLUMNIA

Indeed, you shall not.
Methinks I hear hither your husband's drum,
See him pluck Aufidius down by the hair,
As children from a bear, the Volsces shunning him:
Methinks I see him stamp thus, and call thus:
'Come on, you cowards! you were got in fear,
Though you were born in Rome:' his bloody brow
With his mail'd hand then wiping, forth he goes,
Like to a harvest-man that's task'd to mow
Or all or lose his hire.

VIRGILIA

His bloody brow! O Jupiter, no blood!

VOLUMNIA

Away, you fool! it more becomes a man

Than gilt his trophy: the breasts of Hecuba,
When she did suckle Hector, look'd not lovelier
Than Hector's forehead when it spit forth blood
At Grecian sword, contemning. Tell Valeria,
We are fit to bid her welcome.

(Exit GENTLEWOMAN.)

VIRGILIA

Heavens bless my lord from fell Aufidius!

VOLUMNIA

He'll beat Aufidius' head below his knee
And tread upon his neck.

(Enter VALERIA, with GENTLEWOMAN.)

VALERIA

My ladies both, good day to you.

VOLUMNIA

Sweet madam.

VIRGILIA

I am glad to see your ladyship.

VALERIA

How do you both? you are manifest house-keepers.
What are you sewing here? A fine spot, in good
faith. How does your little son?

VIRGILIA

I thank your ladyship; well, good madam.

VOLUMNIA

He had rather see the swords, and hear a drum, than
look upon his school-master.

VALERIA

O' my word, the father's son: I'll swear, 'tis a
very pretty boy. O' my troth, I looked upon him o'
Wednesday half an hour together: has such a
confirmed countenance. I saw him run after a gilded
butterfly: and when he caught it, he let it go
again; and after it again; and over and over he
comes, and again; catched it again; or whether his
fall enraged him, or how 'twas, he did so set his
teeth and tear it; O, I warrant it, how he mammocked it!

VOLUMNIA

One on 's father's moods.

VALERIA

Indeed, la, 'tis a noble child.

VIRGILIA

A crack, madam.

VALERIA

Come, lay aside your stitchery; I must have you play
the idle huswife with me this afternoon.

VIRGILIA

No, good madam; I will not out of doors.

VALERIA

Not out of doors!

VOLUMNIA

She shall, she shall.

VIRGILIA

Indeed, no, by your patience; I'll not over the
threshold till my lord return from the wars.

VALERIA

Fie, you confine yourself most unreasonably: come,
you must go visit the good lady that lies in.

VIRGILIA

I will wish her speedy strength, and visit her with
my prayers; but I cannot go thither.

VOLUMNIA

Why, I pray you?

VIRGILIA

'Tis not to save labour, nor that I want love.

VALERIA

You would be another Penelope: yet, they say, all
the yarn she spun in Ulysses' absence did but fill
Ithaca full of moths. Come; I would your cambric
were sensible as your finger, that you might leave
pricking it for pity. Come, you shall go with us.

VIRGILIA

No, good madam, pardon me; indeed, I will not forth.

VALERIA

In truth, la, go with me; and I'll tell you
excellent news of your husband.

VIRGILIA

O, good madam, there can be none yet.

VALERIA

Verily, I do not jest with you; there came news from
him last night.

VIRGILIA

Indeed, madam?

VALERIA

In earnest, it's true; I heard a senator speak it.
Thus it is: the Volsces have an army forth; against
whom Cominius the general is gone, with one part of
our Roman power: your lord and Titus Lartius are set
down before their city Corioli; they nothing doubt
prevailing and to make it brief wars. This is true,
on mine honour; and so, I pray, go with us.

VIRGILIA

Give me excuse, good madam; I will obey you in every
thing hereafter.

VOLUMNIA

Let her alone, lady: as she is now, she will but
disease our better mirth.

VALERIA

In troth, I think she would. Fare you well, then.
Come, good sweet lady. Prithee, Virgilia, turn thy
solemness out o' door. and go along with us.

VIRGILIA

No, at a word, madam; indeed, I must not. I wish
you much mirth.

VALERIA

Well, then, farewell.

(Exeunt.)

LOVE'S LABOUR'S LOST

Act 5, Scene 2
4 Characters: 4 female
Princess, Katherine, Rosaline, Maria

The Princess shows her ladies a jewel and some poetry sent to her by King Ferdinand in his efforts to court her. Rosaline then shows her own gifts from Biron, Katherine shows her gifts from Dumaine, and Maria shows the pearls sent by Longaville. The women mock their gifts and men's belief that their affections can be so easily won.

———➤◆◄———

The King of Navarre's Park. Enter the PRINCESS,
KATHARINE, ROSALINE, and MARIA.

PRINCESS
    Sweet hearts, we shall be rich ere we depart,
    If fairings come thus plentifully in:
    A lady wall'd about with diamonds!
    Look you what I have from the loving king.

ROSALINE
    Madame, came nothing else along with that?

PRINCESS
    Nothing but this! yes, as much love in rhyme
    As would be cramm'd up in a sheet of paper,
    Writ o' both sides the leaf, margent and all,
    That he was fain to seal on Cupid's name.

ROSALINE
    That was the way to make his godhead wax,
    For he hath been five thousand years a boy.

KATHARINE

Ay, and a shrewd unhappy gallows too.

ROSALINE

You'll ne'er be friends with him; a' kill'd your sister.

KATHARINE

He made her melancholy, sad, and heavy;
And so she died: had she been light, like you,
Of such a merry, nimble, stirring spirit,
She might ha' been a grandam ere she died:
And so may you; for a light heart lives long.

ROSALINE

What's your dark meaning, mouse, of this light word?

KATHARINE

A light condition in a beauty dark.

ROSALINE

We need more light to find your meaning out.

KATHARINE

You'll mar the light by taking it in snuff;
Therefore I'll darkly end the argument.

ROSALINE

Look what you do, you do it still i' the dark.

KATHARINE

So do not you, for you are a light wench.

ROSALINE

Indeed I weigh not you, and therefore light.

KATHARINE

    You weigh me not? O, that's you care not for me.

ROSALINE

    Great reason; for 'past cure is still past care.'

PRINCESS

    Well bandied both; a set of wit well play'd.
    But Rosaline, you have a favour too:
    Who sent it? and what is it?

ROSALINE

    I would you knew:
    An if my face were but as fair as yours,
    My favour were as great; be witness this.
    Nay, I have verses too, I thank Biron:
    The numbers true; and, were the numbering too,
    I were the fairest goddess on the ground:
    I am compared to twenty thousand fairs.
    O, he hath drawn my picture in his letter!

PRINCESS

    Any thing like?

ROSALINE

    Much in the letters; nothing in the praise.

PRINCESS

    Beauteous as ink; a good conclusion.

KATHARINE

    Fair as a text B in a copy-book.

ROSALINE

    'Ware pencils, ho! let me not die your debtor,
    My red dominical, my golden letter:
    O, that your face were not so full of O's!

KATHARINE

A pox of that jest! and I beshrew all shrows.

PRINCESS

But, Katharine, what was sent to you from fair Dumain?

KATHARINE

Madam, this glove.

PRINCESS

Did he not send you twain?

KATHARINE

Yes, madam, and moreover
Some thousand verses of a faithful lover,
A huge translation of hypocrisy,
Vilely compiled, profound simplicity.

MARIA

This and these pearls to me sent Longaville:
The letter is too long by half a mile.

PRINCESS

I think no less. Dost thou not wish in heart
The chain were longer and the letter short?

MARIA

Ay, or I would these hands might never part.

PRINCESS

We are wise girls to mock our lovers so.

ROSALINE

They are worse fools to purchase mocking so.
That same Biron I'll torture ere I go:
O that I knew he were but in by the week!

How I would make him fawn and beg and seek
And wait the season and observe the times
And spend his prodigal wits in bootless rhymes
And shape his service wholly to my hests
And make him proud to make me proud that jests!
So perttaunt-like would I o'ersway his state
That he should be my fool and I his fate.

PRINCESS

None are so surely caught, when they are catch'd,
As wit turn'd fool: folly, in wisdom hatch'd,
Hath wisdom's warrant and the help of school
And wit's own grace to grace a learned fool.

ROSALINE

The blood of youth burns not with such excess
As gravity's revolt to wantonness.

MARIA

Folly in fools bears not so strong a note
As foolery in the wise, when wit doth dote;
Since all the power thereof it doth apply
To prove, by wit, worth in simplicity.

PRINCESS

Here comes Boyet, and mirth is in his face.

A MIDSUMMER NIGHT'S DREAM

Act 2, Scene 1
4 Characters: 1 male, 1 female, 2 male or female
Oberon (M), Titania (F), Puck (M/F), Fairy (M/F)

An introduction to the fairies of the play who will put spells on the human characters and set in motion the narrative events.

———➤•◀———

A wood near Athens. Enter, from opposite sides, a FAIRY and PUCK.

PUCK

How now, spirit! whither wander you?

FAIRY

Over hill, over dale,
Thorough bush, thorough brier,
Over park, over pale,
Thorough flood, thorough fire,
I do wander everywhere,
Swifter than the moon's sphere;
And I serve the fairy queen,
To dew her orbs upon the green.
The cowslips tall her pensioners be:
In their gold coats spots you see;
Those be rubies, fairy favours,
In those freckles live their savours:
I must go seek some dewdrops here
And hang a pearl in every cowslip's ear.
Farewell, thou lob of spirits; I'll be gone:
Our queen and all our elves come here anon.

PUCK

The king doth keep his revels here to-night:

Take heed the queen come not within his sight;
For Oberon is passing fell and wrath,
Because that she as her attendant hath
A lovely boy, stolen from an Indian king;
She never had so sweet a changeling;
And jealous Oberon would have the child
Knight of his train, to trace the forests wild;
But she perforce withholds the loved boy,
Crowns him with flowers and makes him all her joy:
And now they never meet in grove or green,
By fountain clear, or spangled starlight sheen,
But, they do square, that all their elves for fear
Creep into acorn-cups and hide them there.

FAIRY

Either I mistake your shape and making quite,
Or else you are that shrewd and knavish sprite
Call'd Robin Goodfellow: are not you he
That frights the maidens of the villagery;
Skim milk, and sometimes labour in the quern
And bootless make the breathless housewife churn;
And sometime make the drink to bear no barm;
Mislead night-wanderers, laughing at their harm?
Those that Hobgoblin call you and sweet Puck,
You do their work, and they shall have good luck:
Are not you he?

PUCK

Thou speak'st aright;
I am that merry wanderer of the night.
I jest to Oberon and make him smile
When I a fat and bean-fed horse beguile,
Neighing in likeness of a filly foal:
And sometime lurk I in a gossip's bowl,
In very likeness of a roasted crab,
And when she drinks, against her lips I bob

And on her wither'd dewlap pour the ale.
The wisest aunt, telling the saddest tale,
Sometime for three-foot stool mistaketh me;
Then slip I from her bum, down topples she,
And 'tailor' cries, and falls into a cough;
And then the whole quire hold their hips and laugh,
And waxen in their mirth and neeze and swear
A merrier hour was never wasted there.
But, room, fairy! here comes Oberon.

FAIRY

And here my mistress. Would that he were gone!

(Enter, from one side, OBERON, with his train; from the other, TITANIA, with hers.)

OBERON

Ill met by moonlight, proud Titania.

TITANIA

What, jealous Oberon! Fairies, skip hence:
I have forsworn his bed and company.

OBERON

Tarry, rash wanton: am not I thy lord?

TITANIA

Then I must be thy lady: but I know
When thou hast stolen away from fairy land,
And in the shape of Corin sat all day,
Playing on pipes of corn and versing love
To amorous Phillida. Why art thou here,
Come from the farthest Steppe of India?
But that, forsooth, the bouncing Amazon,
Your buskin'd mistress and your warrior love,
To Theseus must be wedded, and you come
To give their bed joy and prosperity.

OBERON

> How canst thou thus for shame, Titania,
> Glance at my credit with Hippolyta,
> Knowing I know thy love to Theseus?
> Didst thou not lead him through the glimmering night
> From Perigenia, whom he ravished?
> And make him with fair Ægle break his faith,
> With Ariadne and Antiopa?

TITANIA

> These are the forgeries of jealousy:
> And never, since the middle summer's spring,
> Met we on hill, in dale, forest or mead,
> By paved fountain or by rushy brook,
> Or in the beached margent of the sea,
> To dance our ringlets to the whistling wind,
> But with thy brawls thou hast disturb'd our sport.
> Therefore the winds, piping to us in vain,
> As in revenge, have suck'd up from the sea
> Contagious fogs; which falling in the land
> Have every pelting river made so proud
> That they have overborne their continents:
> The ox hath therefore stretch'd his yoke in vain,
> The ploughman lost his sweat, and the green corn
> Hath rotted ere his youth attain'd a beard;
> The fold stands empty in the drowned field,
> And crows are fatted with the murrion flock;
> The nine men's morris is fill'd up with mud,
> And the quaint mazes in the wanton green
> For lack of tread are undistinguishable:
> The human mortals want their winter here;
> No night is now with hymn or carol blest:
> Therefore the moon, the governess of floods,
> Pale in her anger, washes all the air,
> That rheumatic diseases do abound:
> And thorough this distemperature we see
> The seasons alter: hoary-headed frosts

Far in the fresh lap of the crimson rose,
And on old Hiems' thin and icy crown
An odorous chaplet of sweet summer buds
Is, as in mockery, set: the spring, the summer,
The childing autumn, angry winter, change
Their wonted liveries, and the mazed world,
By their increase, now knows not which is which:
And this same progeny of evils comes
From our debate, from our dissension;
We are their parents and original.

OBERON

Do you amend it then; it lies in you:
Why should Titania cross her Oberon?
I do but beg a little changeling boy,
To be my henchman.

TITANIA

Set your heart at rest:
The fairy land buys not the child of me.
His mother was a votaress of my order:
And, in the spiced Indian air, by night,
Full often hath she gossip'd by my side,
And sat with me on Neptune's yellow sands,
Marking the embarked traders on the flood,
When we have laugh'd to see the sails conceive
And grow big-bellied with the wanton wind;
Which she, with pretty and with swimming gait
Following, — her womb then rich with my young squire, —
Would imitate, and sail upon the land,
To fetch me trifles, and return again,
As from a voyage, rich with merchandise.
But she, being mortal, of that boy did die;
And for her sake do I rear up her boy,
And for her sake I will not part with him.

OBERON

> How long within this wood intend you stay?

TITANIA

> Perchance till after Theseus' wedding-day.
> If you will patiently dance in our round
> And see our moonlight revels, go with us;
> If not, shun me, and I will spare your haunts.

OBERON

> Give me that boy, and I will go with thee.

TITANIA

> Not for thy fairy kingdom. Fairies, away!
> We shall chide downright, if I longer stay.

> *(Exit TITANIA with her train.)*

OBERON

> Well, go thy way: thou shalt not from this grove
> Till I torment thee for this injury.
> My gentle Puck, come hither. Thou rememberest
> Since once I sat upon a promontory,
> And heard a mermaid on a dolphin's back
> Uttering such dulcet and harmonious breath
> That the rude sea grew civil at her song
> And certain stars shot madly from their spheres,
> To hear the sea-maid's music.

PUCK

> I remember.

OBERON

> That very time I saw, but thou couldst not,
> Flying between the cold moon and the earth,
> Cupid all arm'd: a certain aim he took
> At a fair vestal throned by the west,
> And loosed his love-shaft smartly from his bow,

As it should pierce a hundred thousand hearts;
But I might see young Cupid's fiery shaft
Quench'd in the chaste beams of the watery moon,
And the imperial votaress passed on,
In maiden meditation, fancy-free.
Yet mark'd I where the bolt of Cupid fell:
It fell upon a little western flower,
Before milk-white, now purple with love's wound,
And maidens call it love-in-idleness.
Fetch me that flower; the herb I shew'd thee once:
The juice of it on sleeping eye-lids laid
Will make or man or woman madly dote
Upon the next live creature that it sees.
Fetch me this herb; and be thou here again
Ere the leviathan can swim a league.

PUCK

I'll put a girdle round about the earth
In forty minutes.

(Exit.)

OBERON

Having once this juice,
I'll watch Titania when she is asleep,
And drop the liquor of it in her eyes.
The next thing then she waking looks upon,
Be it on lion, bear, or wolf, or bull,
On meddling monkey, or on busy ape,
She shall pursue it with the soul of love:
And ere I take this charm from off her sight,
As I can take it with another herb,
I'll make her render up her page to me.
But who comes here? I am invisible;
And I will overhear their conference.

SCENES FOR
FIVE OR MORE
CHARACTERS

LOVE'S LABOUR'S LOST

Act 4, Scene 1
5 Characters: 3 female, 2 female
Rosaline (F), Katherine (F), Maria (F), Boyet (M), Costard (M)

While the Princess and her ladies were hunting, the clownish Costard gave the Princess the letter from Armado meant for Jaquenetta, mistakenly thinking it was the letter for Rosaline from Biron. The Princess exits, and amid the confusion, Boyet flirts unsuccessfully with Rosaline.

———◦———

Exeunt PRINCESS and train.

BOYET
    Who is the suitor? who is the suitor?

ROSALINE
    Shall I teach you to know?

BOYET
    Ay, my continent of beauty.

ROSALINE
    Why, she that bears the bow.
    Finely put off!

BOYET
    My lady goes to kill horns; but, if thou marry,
    Hang me by the neck, if horns that year miscarry.
    Finely put on!

ROSALINE
    Well, then, I am the shooter.

BOYET

And who is your deer?

ROSALINE

If we choose by the horns, yourself come not near.
Finely put on, indeed!

MARIA

You still wrangle with her, Boyet, and she strikes
at the brow.

BOYET

But she herself is hit lower: have I hit her now?

ROSALINE

Shall I come upon thee with an old saying, that was
a man when King Pepin of France was a little boy, as
touching the hit it?

BOYET

So I may answer thee with one as old, that was a
woman when Queen Guinover of Britain was a little
wench, as touching the hit it.

ROSALINE

Thou canst not hit it, hit it, hit it,
Thou canst not hit it, my good man.

BOYET

An I cannot, cannot, cannot,
An I cannot, another can.

(Exeunt ROSALINE and KATHARINE.)

COSTARD

By my troth, most pleasant: how both did fit it!

MARIA

A mark marvellous well shot, for they both did hit it.

BOYET

A mark! O, mark but that mark! A mark, says my lady!
Let the mark have a prick in't, to mete at, if it may be.

MARIA

Wide o' the bow hand! i' faith, your hand is out.

COSTARD

Indeed, a' must shoot nearer, or he'll ne'er hit the clout.

BOYET

An if my hand be out, then belike your hand is in.

COSTARD

Then will she get the upshoot by cleaving the pin.

MARIA

Come, come, you talk greasily; your lips grow foul.

COSTARD

She's too hard for you at pricks, sir: challenge her to bowl.

BOYET

I fear too much rubbing. Good night, my good owl.

(Exeunt BOYET and MARIA.)

COSTARD

By my soul, a swain! a most simple clown!
Lord, Lord, how the ladies and I have put him down!
O' my troth, most sweet jests! most incony
vulgar wit!
When it comes so smoothly off, so obscenely, as it

were, so fit.
Armado o' th' one side, — O, a most dainty man!
To see him walk before a lady and to bear her fan!
To see him kiss his hand! and how most sweetly a'
will swear!
And his page o' t' other side, that handful of wit!
Ah, heavens, it is a most pathetical nit!
Sola, sola!

(Shout within.)
(Exit COSTARD, running.)

MACBETH

Act 1, Scene 3
5 Characters: 3 female, 2 male
3 Witches (F), Macbeth (M), Banquo (M)

Three witches discuss evil spells they have recently made as they wait to intercept Macbeth and Banquo on their way home from battle. The witches prophesy about the future of Macbeth and Banquo, planting the seeds of treachery in Macbeth with their prediction that he will be King of Scotland.

———————

A heath near Forres. Thunder. Enter the three WITCHES.

FIRST WITCH
>Where hast thou been, sister?

SECOND WITCH
>Killing swine.

THIRD WITCH
>Sister, where thou?

FIRST WITCH
>A sailor's wife had chestnuts in her lap,
>And munch'd, and munch'd, and munch'd: —
>'Give me,' quoth I:
>'Aroint thee, witch!' the rump-fed ronyon cries.
>Her husband's to Aleppo gone, master o' the Tiger:
>But in a sieve I'll thither sail,
>And, like a rat without a tail,
>I'll do, I'll do, and I'll do.

SECOND WITCH
>I'll give thee a wind.

FIRST WITCH
     Thou'rt kind.

THIRD WITCH
     And I another.

FIRST WITCH
     I myself have all the other,
     And the very ports they blow,
     All the quarters that they know
     I' the shipman's card.
     I will drain him dry as hay:
     Sleep shall neither night nor day
     Hang upon his pent-house lid;
     He shall live a man forbid:
     Weary se'nnights nine times nine
     Shall he dwindle, peak and pine:
     Though his bark cannot be lost,
     Yet it shall be tempest-tost.
     Look what I have.

SECOND WITCH
     Show me, show me.

FIRST WITCH
     Here I have a pilot's thumb,
     Wreck'd as homeward he did come.

     (Drum within.)

THIRD WITCH
     A drum, a drum!
     Macbeth doth come.

ALL
     The weird sisters, hand in hand,

Posters of the sea and land,
Thus do go about, about:
Thrice to thine and thrice to mine
And thrice again, to make up nine.
Peace! the charm's wound up.

(Enter MACBETH and BANQUO.)

MACBETH

So foul and fair a day I have not seen.

BANQUO

How far is't call'd to Forres? What are these
So wither'd and so wild in their attire,
That look not like the inhabitants o' the earth,
And yet are on't? Live you? or are you aught
That man may question? You seem to understand me,
By each at once her chappy finger laying
Upon her skinny lips: you should be women,
And yet your beards forbid me to interpret
That you are so.

MACBETH

Speak, if you can: what are you?

FIRST WITCH

All hail, Macbeth! hail to thee, thane of Glamis!

SECOND WITCH

All hail, Macbeth, hail to thee, thane of Cawdor!

THIRD WITCH

All hail, Macbeth, thou shalt be king hereafter!

BANQUO

Good sir, why do you start; and seem to fear

Things that do sound so fair? I' the name of truth,
Are ye fantastical, or that indeed
Which outwardly ye show? My noble partner
You greet with present grace and great prediction
Of noble having and of royal hope,
That he seems rapt withal: to me you speak not.
If you can look into the seeds of time,
And say which grain will grow and which will not,
Speak then to me, who neither beg nor fear
Your favours nor your hate.

FIRST WITCH
Hail!

SECOND WITCH
Hail!

THIRD WITCH
Hail!

FIRST WITCH
Lesser than Macbeth, and greater.

SECOND WITCH
Not so happy, yet much happier.

THIRD WITCH
Thou shalt get kings, though thou be none:
So all hail, Macbeth and Banquo!

FIRST WITCH
Banquo and Macbeth, all hail!

MACBETH
Stay, you imperfect speakers, tell me more:
By Sinel's death I know I am thane of Glamis;

But how of Cawdor? the thane of Cawdor lives,
A prosperous gentleman; and to be king
Stands not within the prospect of belief,
No more than to be Cawdor. Say from whence
You owe this strange intelligence? or why
Upon this blasted heath you stop our way
With such prophetic greeting? Speak, I charge you.

(WITCHES vanish.)

MUCH ADO ABOUT NOTHING

Act 2, Scene 3
5 Characters: 4 male, 1 female
Don Pedro (M), Claudio (M), Leonato (M), Benedick (M), Beatrice (F)

Benedick, hiding in the orchard, overhears Don Pedro, Claudio, and
Leonato talking about Beatrice's love for him; they, of course, are
completely aware he is listening. They leave and Beatrice enters to
call Benedick to dinner; she is her usual caustic self, but now
Benedick is convinced she really loves him.

───➤●◄───

Leonato's orchard.

DON PEDRO
> Come hither, Leonato. What was it you told me of
> to-day, that your niece Beatrice was in love with
> Signior Benedick?

CLAUDIO
> O, ay: stalk on, stalk on; the fowl sits. I did
> never think that lady would have loved any man.

LEONATO
> No, nor I neither; but most wonderful that she
> should so dote on Signior Benedick, whom she hath in
> all outward behaviors seemed ever to abhor.

BENEDICK
> Is't possible? Sits the wind in that corner?

LEONATO
> By my troth, my lord, I cannot tell what to think
> of it but that she loves him with an enraged
> affection: it is past the infinite of thought.

DON PEDRO

May be she doth but counterfeit.

CLAUDIO

Faith, like enough.

LEONATO

O God, counterfeit! There was never counterfeit of passion came so near the life of passion as she discovers it.

DON PEDRO

Why, what effects of passion shows she?

CLAUDIO

Bait the hook well; this fish will bite.

LEONATO

What effects, my lord? She will sit you, you heard my daughter tell you how.

CLAUDIO

She did, indeed.

DON PEDRO

How, how, pray you? You amaze me: I would have I thought her spirit had been invincible against all assaults of affection.

LEONATO

I would have sworn it had, my lord; especially against Benedick.

BENEDICK

I should think this a gull, but that the white-bearded fellow speaks it: knavery cannot, sure, hide himself in such reverence.

CLAUDIO

He hath ta'en the infection: hold it up.

DON PEDRO

    Hath she made her affection known to Benedick?

LEONATO

    No; and swears she never will: that's her torment.

CLAUDIO

    'Tis true, indeed; so your daughter says: 'Shall
    I,' says she, 'that have so oft encountered him
    with scorn, write to him that I love him?'

LEONATO

    This says she now when she is beginning to write to
    him; for she'll be up twenty times a night, and
    there will she sit in her smock till she have writ a
    sheet of paper: my daughter tells us all.

CLAUDIO

    Now you talk of a sheet of paper, I remember a
    pretty jest your daughter told us of.

LEONATO

    O, when she had writ it and was reading it over, she
    found Benedick and Beatrice between the sheet?

CLAUDIO

    That.

LEONATO

    O, she tore the letter into a thousand halfpence;
    railed at herself, that she should be so immodest
    to write to one that she knew would flout her; 'I
    measure him,' says she, 'by my own spirit; for I
    should flout him, if he writ to me; yea, though I
    love him, I should.'

CLAUDIO

    Then down upon her knees she falls, weeps, sobs,
    beats her heart, tears her hair, prays, curses; 'O
    sweet Benedick! God give me patience!'

LEONATO

She doth indeed; my daughter says so: and the
ecstasy hath so much overborne her that my daughter
is sometime afeared she will do a desperate outrage
to herself: it is very true.

DON PEDRO

It were good that Benedick knew of it by some
other, if she will not discover it.

CLAUDIO

To what end? He would make but a sport of it and
torment the poor lady worse.

DON PEDRO

An he should, it were an alms to hang him. She's an
excellent sweet lady; and, out of all suspicion,
she is virtuous.

CLAUDIO

And she is exceeding wise.

DON PEDRO

In every thing but in loving Benedick.

LEONATO

O, my lord, wisdom and blood combating in so tender
a body, we have ten proofs to one that blood hath
the victory. I am sorry for her, as I have just
cause, being her uncle and her guardian.

DON PEDRO

I would she had bestowed this dotage on me: I would
have daffed all other respects and made her half
myself. I pray you, tell Benedick of it, and hear
what a' will say.

LEONATO

Were it good, think you?

CLAUDIO

Hero thinks surely she will die; for she says she
will die, if he love her not, and she will die, ere
she make her love known, and she will die, if he woo
her, rather than she will bate one breath of her
accustomed crossness.

DON PEDRO

She doth well: if she should make tender of her
love, 'tis very possible he'll scorn it; for the
man, as you know all, hath a contemptible spirit.

CLAUDIO

He is a very proper man.

DON PEDRO

He hath indeed a good outward happiness.

CLAUDIO

Before God! and, in my mind, very wise.

DON PEDRO

He doth indeed show some sparks that are like wit.

CLAUDIO

And I take him to be valiant.

DON PEDRO

As Hector, I assure you: and in the managing of
quarrels you may say he is wise; for either he
avoids them with great discretion, or undertakes
them with a most Christian-like fear.

LEONATO

If he do fear God, a' must necessarily keep peace:
if he break the peace, he ought to enter into a
quarrel with fear and trembling.

DON PEDRO

And so will he do; for the man doth fear God,
howsoever it seems not in him by some large jests
he will make. Well I am sorry for your niece. Shall
we go seek Benedick, and tell him of her love?

CLAUDIO

Never tell him, my lord: let her wear it out with
good counsel.

LEONATO

Nay, that's impossible: she may wear her heart out first.

DON PEDRO

Well, we will hear further of it by your daughter:
let it cool the while. I love Benedick well; and I
could wish he would modestly examine himself, to see
how much he is unworthy so good a lady.

LEONATO

My lord, will you walk? dinner is ready.

CLAUDIO

If he do not dote on her upon this, I will never
trust my expectation.

DON PEDRO

Let there be the same net spread for her; and that
must your daughter and her gentlewomen carry. The
sport will be, when they hold one an opinion of
another's dotage, and no such matter: that's the
scene that I would see, which will be merely a
dumb-show. Let us send her to call him in to dinner.

(Exeunt DON PEDRO, CLAUDIO, and LEONATO.)

BENEDICK

(Coming forward.) This can be no trick: the
conference was sadly borne. They have the truth of

this from Hero. They seem to pity the lady: it
seems her affections have their full bent. Love me!
why, it must be requited. I hear how I am censured:
they say I will bear myself proudly, if I perceive
the love come from her; they say too that she will
rather die than give any sign of affection. I did
never think to marry: I must not seem proud: happy
are they that hear their detractions and can put
them to mending. They say the lady is fair; 'tis a
truth, I can bear them witness; and virtuous; 'tis
so, I cannot reprove it; and wise, but for loving
me; by my troth, it is no addition to her wit, nor
no great argument of her folly, for I will be
horribly in love with her. I may chance have some
odd quirks and remnants of wit broken on me,
because I have railed so long against marriage: but
doth not the appetite alter? a man loves the meat
in his youth that he cannot endure in his age.
Shall quips and sentences and these paper bullets of
the brain awe a man from the career of his humour?
No, the world must be peopled. When I said I would
die a bachelor, I did not think I should live till I
were married. Here comes Beatrice. By this day!
she's a fair lady: I do spy some marks of love
in her.

(Enter BEATRICE.)

BEATRICE
Against my will I am sent to bid you come in to dinner.

BENEDICK
Fair Beatrice, I thank you for your pains.

BEATRICE
I took no more pains for those thanks than you take
pains to thank me: if it had been painful, I would
not have come.

BENEDICK

You take pleasure then in the message?

BEATRICE

Yea, just so much as you may take upon a knife's
point and choke a daw withal. You have no stomach,
signior: fare you well.

(Exit.)

BENEDICK

Ha! 'Against my will I am sent to bid you come in
to dinner;' there's a double meaning in that 'I took
no more pains for those thanks than you took pains
to thank me'; that's as much as to say, Any pains
that I take for you is as easy as thanks. If I do
not take pity of her, I am a villain. I will go get
her picture.

(Exit.)

TWO GENTLEMEN OF VERONA

Act 4, Scene 2

5 Characters: 3 male, 2 female

Proteus (M), Thurio (M), Host (M), Julia (F), Silvia (F)

While pretending to advance Thurio's courtship of Silvia, Proteus stands beneath Silvia's window and woos her himself. Proteus's girl-friend, Julia (dressed as a boy), watches Proteus in his scheme. Silvia accuses Proteus of being false both to Julia and to his friend, Valentine.

———⟫◦⟪———

Milan. Outside the Duke's palace, under Silvia's chamber.
Enter PROTEUS.

PROTEUS
    Already have I been false to Valentine
    And now I must be as unjust to Thurio.
    Under the colour of commending him,
    I have access my own love to prefer:
    But Silvia is too fair, too true, too holy,
    To be corrupted with my worthless gifts.
    When I protest true loyalty to her,
    She twits me with my falsehood to my friend;
    When to her beauty I commend my vows,
    She bids me think how I have been forsworn
    In breaking faith with Julia whom I loved:
    And notwithstanding all her sudden quips,
    The least whereof would quell a lover's hope,
    Yet, spaniel-like, the more she spurns my love,
    The more it grows and fawneth on her still.
    But here comes Thurio: now must we to her window,
    And give some evening music to her ear.

(Enter THURIO and MUSICIANS.)

THURIO

How now, Sir Proteus, are you crept before us?

PROTEUS

Ay, gentle Thurio: for you know that love
Will creep in service where it cannot go.

THURIO

Ay, but I hope, sir, that you love not here.

PROTEUS

Sir, but I do; or else I would be hence.

THURIO

Who? Silvia?

PROTEUS

Ay, Silvia; for your sake.

THURIO

I thank you for your own. Now, gentlemen,
Let's tune, and to it lustily awhile.

(Enter, at a distance, HOST and JULIA in boy's clothes.)

HOST

Now, my young guest, methinks you're allycholly: I
pray you, why is it?

JULIA

Marry, mine host, because I cannot be merry.

HOST

Come, we'll have you merry: I'll bring you where
you shall hear music and see the gentleman that you asked for.

JULIA

But shall I hear him speak?

HOST

Ay, that you shall.

JULIA

That will be music.

(Music plays.)

HOST

Hark, hark!

JULIA

Is he among these?

HOST

Ay: but, peace! let's hear 'em.

SONG.
Who is Silvia? what is she,
That all our swains commend her?
Holy, fair and wise is she;
The heaven such grace did lend her,
That she might admired be.
Is she kind as she is fair?
For beauty lives with kindness.
Love doth to her eyes repair,
To help him of his blindness,
And, being help'd, inhabits there.
Then to Silvia let us sing,
That Silvia is excelling;
She excels each mortal thing
Upon the dull earth dwelling:
To her let us garlands bring.

HOST

How now! are you sadder than you were before? How
do you, man? the music likes you not.

JULIA

You mistake; the musician likes me not.

HOST

Why, my pretty youth?

JULIA

He plays false, father.

HOST

How? out of tune on the strings?

JULIA

Not so; but yet so false that he grieves my very
heart-strings.

HOST

You have a quick ear.

JULIA

Ay, I would I were deaf; it makes me have a slow heart.

HOST

I perceive you delight not in music.

JULIA

Not a whit, when it jars so.

HOST

Hark, what fine change is in the music!

JULIA

Ay, that change is the spite.

HOST

You would have them always play but one thing?

JULIA

I would always have one play but one thing.
But, host, doth this Sir Proteus that we talk on
Often resort unto this gentlewoman?

HOST

I tell you what Launce, his man, told me: he loved

her out of all nick.

JULIA

Where is Launce?

HOST

Gone to seek his dog; which tomorrow, by his
master's command, he must carry for a present to his lady.

JULIA

Peace! stand aside: the company parts.

PROTEUS

Sir Thurio, fear not you: I will so plead
That you shall say my cunning drift excels.

THURIO

Where meet we?

PROTEUS

At Saint Gregory's well.

THURIO

Farewell.

(Exeunt THURIO and MUSICIANS.)
(Enter SILVIA above.)

PROTEUS

Madam, good even to your ladyship.

SILVIA

I thank you for your music, gentlemen.
Who is that that spake?

PROTEUS

One, lady, if you knew his pure heart's truth,
You would quickly learn to know him by his voice.

SILVIA

Sir Proteus, as I take it.

PROTEUS

> Sir Proteus, gentle lady, and your servant.

SILVIA

> What's your will?

PROTEUS

> That I may compass yours.

SILVIA

> You have your wish; my will is even this:
> That presently you hie you home to bed.
> Thou subtle, perjured, false, disloyal man!
> Think'st thou I am so shallow, so conceitless,
> To be seduced by thy flattery,
> That hast deceived so many with thy vows?
> Return, return, and make thy love amends.
> For me, by this pale queen of night I swear,
> I am so far from granting thy request
> That I despise thee for thy wrongful suit,
> And by and by intend to chide myself
> Even for this time I spend in talking to thee.

PROTEUS

> I grant, sweet love, that I did love a lady;
> But she is dead.

JULIA

> *(Aside.)* 'Twere false, if I should speak it;
> For I am sure she is not buried.

SILVIA

> Say that she be; yet Valentine thy friend
> Survives; to whom, thyself art witness,
> I am betroth'd: and art thou not ashamed
> To wrong him with thy importunacy?

PROTEUS

> I likewise hear that Valentine is dead.

SILVIA

    And so suppose am I; for in his grave
    Assure thyself my love is buried.

PROTEUS

    Sweet lady, let me rake it from the earth.

SILVIA

    Go to thy lady's grave and call hers thence,
    Or, at the least, in hers sepulchre thine.

JULIA

    (Aside.) He heard not that.

PROTEUS

    Madam, if your heart be so obdurate,
    Vouchsafe me yet your picture for my love,
    The picture that is hanging in your chamber;
    To that I'll speak, to that I'll sigh and weep:
    For since the substance of your perfect self
    Is else devoted, I am but a shadow;
    And to your shadow will I make true love.

JULIA

    (Aside.) If 'twere a substance, you would, sure, deceive it,
    And make it but a shadow, as I am.

SILVIA

    I am very loath to be your idol, sir;
    But since your falsehood shall become you well
    To worship shadows and adore false shapes,
    Send to me in the morning and I'll send it:
    And so, good rest.

PROTEUS

    As wretches have o'ernight
    That wait for execution in the morn.

(Exeunt PROTEUS and SILVIA severally.)

JULIA

Host, will you go?

HOST

By my halidom, I was fast asleep.

JULIA

Pray you, where lies Sir Proteus?

HOST

Marry, at my house. Trust me, I think 'tis almost
day.

JULIA

Not so; but it hath been the longest night
That e'er I watch'd and the most heaviest.

(Exeunt.)

A MIDSUMMER NIGHT'S DREAM

Act 3, Scene 1

6 Characters: 1 male, 1 female, 4 male or female
Titania (F), Bottom (M), Peaseblossom (M/F), Cobweb (M/F),
Moth (M/F), Mustardseed (M/F)

Bottom has been rehearsing in the woods with his theater company.
Puck turns his head into that of a donkey, but Bottom is unaware of
the change. Bottom's friends, seeing this, panic and run away, leaving Bottom alone in the woods near where the Fairy Queen, Titania,
is sleeping. She is under a spell that she will fall in love with the first
person she sees when she wakes up.

⋙●⋘

The wood. TITANIA awaking from sleep to BOTTOM
singing.

TITANIA
  (Awaking.) What angel wakes me from my flowery bed?

BOTTOM
  (Sings.) The finch, the sparrow and the lark,
  The plain-song cuckoo gray,
  Whose note full many a man doth mark,
  And dares not answer nay; —
  for, indeed, who would set his wit to so foolish
  a bird? who would give a bird the lie, though he cry
  'cuckoo' never so?

TITANIA
  I pray thee, gentle mortal, sing again:
  Mine ear is much enamour'd of thy note;
  So is mine eye enthralled to thy shape;
  And thy fair virtue's force perforce doth move me
  On the first view to say, to swear, I love thee.

BOTTOM

Methinks, mistress, you should have little reason
for that: and yet, to say the truth, reason and
love keep little company together now-a-days; the
more the pity that some honest neighbours will not
make them friends. Nay, I can gleek upon occasion.

TITANIA

Thou art as wise as thou art beautiful.

BOTTOM

Not so, neither: but if I had wit enough to get out
of this wood, I have enough to serve mine own turn.

TITANIA

Out of this wood do not desire to go:
Thou shalt remain here, whether thou wilt or no.
I am a spirit of no common rate;
The summer still doth tend upon my state;
And I do love thee: therefore, go with me;
I'll give thee fairies to attend on thee,
And they shall fetch thee jewels from the deep,
And sing while thou on pressed flowers dost sleep;
And I will purge thy mortal grossness so
That thou shalt like an airy spirit go.
Peaseblossom! Cobweb! Moth! and Mustardseed!

(Enter PEASEBLOSSOM, COBWEB, MOTH, and
MUSTARDSEED.)

PEASEBLOSSOM

Ready.

COBWEB

And I.

MOTH
>And I.

MUSTARDSEED
>And I.

ALL
>Where shall we go?

TITANIA
>Be kind and courteous to this gentleman;
>Hop in his walks and gambol in his eyes;
>Feed him with apricocks and dewberries,
>With purple grapes, green figs, and mulberries;
>The honey-bags steal from the humble-bees,
>And for night-tapers crop their waxen thighs
>And light them at the fiery glow-worm's eyes,
>To have my love to bed and to arise;
>And pluck the wings from Painted butterflies
>To fan the moonbeams from his sleeping eyes:
>Nod to him, elves, and do him courtesies.

PEASEBLOSSOM
>Hail, mortal!

COBWEB
>Hail!

MOTH
>Hail!

MUSTARDSEED
>Hail!

BOTTOM
>I cry your worship's mercy, heartily: I beseech your
>worship's name.

COBWEB
Cobweb.

BOTTOM
I shall desire you of more acquaintance, good Master
Cobweb: if I cut my finger, I shall make bold with
you. Your name, honest gentleman?

PEASEBLOSSOM
Peaseblossom.

BOTTOM
I pray you, commend me to Mistress Squash, your
mother, and to Master Peascod, your father. Good
Master Peaseblossom, I shall desire you of more
acquaintance too. Your name, I beseech you, sir?

MUSTARDSEED
Mustardseed.

BOTTOM
Good Master Mustardseed, I know your patience well:
that same cowardly, giant-like ox-beef hath
devoured many a gentleman of your house: I promise
you your kindred had made my eyes water ere now. I
desire your more acquaintance, good Master
Mustardseed.

TITANIA
Come, wait upon him; lead him to my bower.
The moon methinks looks with a watery eye;
And when she weeps, weeps every little flower,
Lamenting some enforced chastity.
Tie up my love's tongue bring him silently.

(Exeunt.)

A MIDSUMMER NIGHT'S DREAM,

Act 1, Scene 2
6 Characters: 6 male
Bottom, Quince, Snug, Flute, Snout, Starveling

The Rude Mechanicals, a group of tradesmen, meet for their first rehearsal and assign parts for the play they are to present at the wedding of the Duke and Duchess.

———➤•◄———

Athens. Quince's house. Enter QUINCE, SNUG, BOTTOM, FLUTE, SNOUT, and STARVELING.

QUINCE
> Is all our company here?

BOTTOM
> You were best to call them generally, man by man, according to the scrip.

QUINCE
> Here is the scroll of every man's name, which is thought fit, through all Athens, to play in our interlude before the duke and the duchess, on his wedding-day at night.

BOTTOM
> First, good Peter Quince, say what the play treats on, then read the names of the actors, and so grow to a point.

QUINCE
> Marry, our play is, The most lamentable comedy, and most cruel death of Pyramus and Thisbe.

BOTTOM

A very good piece of work, I assure you, and a
merry. Now, good Peter Quince, call forth your
actors by the scroll. Masters, spread yourselves.

QUINCE

Answer as I call you. Nick Bottom, the weaver.

BOTTOM

Ready. Name what part I am for, and proceed.

QUINCE

You, Nick Bottom, are set down for Pyramus.

BOTTOM

What is Pyramus? a lover, or a tyrant?

QUINCE

A lover, that kills himself most gallant for love.

BOTTOM

That will ask some tears in the true performing of
it: if I do it, let the audience look to their
eyes; I will move storms, I will condole in some
measure. To the rest: yet my chief humour is for a
tyrant: I could play Ercles rarely, or a part to
tear a cat in, to make all split.
The raging rocks
And shivering shocks
Shall break the locks
Of prison gates;
And Phibbus' car
Shall shine from far
And make and mar
The foolish Fates.
This was lofty! Now name the rest of the players.

This is Ercles' vein, a tyrant's vein; a lover is
more condoling.

QUINCE

Francis Flute, the bellows-mender.

FLUTE

Here, Peter Quince.

QUINCE

Flute, you must take Thisbe on you.

FLUTE

What is Thisbe? a wandering knight?

QUINCE

It is the lady that Pyramus must love.

FLUTE

Nay, faith, let me not play a woman; I have a beard coming.

QUINCE

That's all one: you shall play it in a mask, and
you may speak as small as you will.

BOTTOM

An I may hide my face, let me play Thisne too, I'll
speak in a monstrous little voice. 'Thisne,
Thisne'; 'Ah, Pyramus, lover dear! thy Thisbe dear,
and lady dear!'

QUINCE

No, no; you must play Pyramus: and, Flute, you Thisbe.

BOTTOM

Well, proceed.

QUINCE

Robin Starveling, the tailor.

STARVELING

Here, Peter Quince.

QUINCE

Robin Starveling, you must play Thisbe's mother.
Tom Snout, the tinker.

SNOUT

Here, Peter Quince.

QUINCE

You, Pyramus' father: myself, Thisbe's father:
Snug, the joiner; you, the lion's part: and, I
hope, here is a play fitted.

SNUG

Have you the lion's part written? pray you, if it
be, give it me, for I am slow of study.

QUINCE

You may do it extempore, for it is nothing but roaring.

BOTTOM

Let me play the lion too: I will roar, that I will
do any man's heart good to hear me; I will roar,
that I will make the duke say 'Let him roar again,
let him roar again.'

QUINCE

An you should do it too terribly, you would fright
the duchess and the ladies, that they would shriek;
and that were enough to hang us all.

ALL

    That would hang us, every mother's son.

BOTTOM

    I grant you, friends, if that you should fright the
    ladies out of their wits, they would have no more
    discretion but to hang us: but I will aggravate my
    voice so that I will roar you as gently as any
    sucking dove; I will roar you an 'twere any
    nightingale.

QUINCE

    You can play no part but Pyramus; for Pyramus is a
    sweet-faced man; a proper man, as one shall see in a
    summer's day; a most lovely gentleman-like man:
    therefore you must needs play Pyramus.

BOTTOM

    Well, I will undertake it. What beard were I best
    to play it in?

QUINCE

    Why, what you will.

BOTTOM

    I will discharge it in either your straw-colour
    beard, your orange-tawny beard, your purple-in-grain
    beard, or your French-crown-colour beard, your
    perfect yellow.

QUINCE

    Some of your French crowns have no hair at all, and
    then you will play bare-faced. But, masters, here
    are your parts: and I am to entreat you, request
    you and desire you, to con them by to-morrow night;
    and meet me in the palace wood, a mile without the

town, by moonlight; there will we rehearse, for if
we meet in the city, we shall be dogged with
company, and our devices known. In the meantime I
will draw a bill of properties, such as our play
wants. I pray you, fail me not.

BOTTOM

We will meet; and there we may rehearse most
obscenely and courageously. Take pains; be perfect: adieu.

QUINCE

At the duke's oak we meet.

BOTTOM

Enough; hold or cut bow-strings.

(Exeunt.)

MACBETH

Act 3, Scene 4

6 Characters: 5 male, 1 female

Macbeth (M), Ross (M), Lennox (M), Lord (M), Ghost of Banquo (M), Lady Macbeth (F)

After having had Banquo killed, Macbeth thinks he sees Banquo's ghost sitting at the table.

⸺➤◆◀⸺

A Hall in the palace. A banquet prepared.

LADY MACBETH

>My royal lord,
>You do not give the cheer: the feast is sold
>That is not often vouch'd, while 'tis a-making,
>'Tis given with welcome: to feed were best at home;
>From thence the sauce to meat is ceremony;
>Meeting were bare without it.

MACBETH

>Sweet remembrancer!
>Now, good digestion wait on appetite,
>And health on both!

LENNOX

>May't please your highness sit.

>*(The GHOST OF BANQUO enters and sits in MACBETH's place.)*

MACBETH

>Here had we now our country's honour roof'd,
>Were the graced person of our Banquo present;

Who may I rather challenge for unkindness
Than pity for mischance!

ROSS

His absence, sir,
Lays blame upon his promise. Please't your highness
To grace us with your royal company.

MACBETH

The table's full.

LENNOX

Here is a place reserved, sir.

MACBETH

Where?

LENNOX

Here, my good lord. What is't that moves your highness?

MACBETH

Which of you have done this?

LORD

What, my good lord?

MACBETH

Thou canst not say I did it: never shake
Thy gory locks at me.

ROSS

Gentlemen, rise: his highness is not well.

LADY MACBETH

Sit, worthy friends: my lord is often thus,

And hath been from his youth: pray you, keep seat;
The fit is momentary; upon a thought
He will again be well: if much you note him,
You shall offend him and extend his passion:
Feed, and regard him not. Are you a man?

MACBETH

Ay, and a bold one, that dare look on that
Which might appal the devil.

LADY MACBETH

O proper stuff!
This is the very painting of your fear:
This is the air-drawn dagger which, you said,
Led you to Duncan. O, these flaws and starts,
Impostors to true fear, would well become
A woman's story at a winter's fire,
Authorized by her grandam. Shame itself!
Why do you make such faces? When all's done,
You look but on a stool.

MACBETH

Prithee, see there! behold! look! lo!
how say you?
Why, what care I? If thou canst nod, speak too.
If charnel-houses and our graves must send
Those that we bury back, our monuments
Shall be the maws of kites.

(GHOST OF BANQUO vanishes.)

LADY MACBETH

What, quite unmann'd in folly?

MACBETH

If I stand here, I saw him.

LADY MACBETH

Fie, for shame!

MACBETH

Blood hath been shed ere now, i' the olden time,
Ere human statute purged the gentle weal;
Ay, and since too, murders have been perform'd
Too terrible for the ear: the times have been,
That, when the brains were out, the man would die,
And there an end; but now they rise again,
With twenty mortal murders on their crowns,
And push us from our stools: this is more strange
Than such a murder is.

LADY MACBETH

My worthy lord,
Your noble friends do lack you.

MACBETH

I do forget.
Do not muse at me, my most worthy friends,
I have a strange infirmity, which is nothing
To those that know me. Come, love and health to all;
Then I'll sit down. Give me some wine; fill full.
I drink to the general joy o' the whole table,
And to our dear friend Banquo, whom we miss;
Would he were here! to all, and him, we thirst,
And all to all.

LORD

Our duties, and the pledge.

(Re-enter GHOST OF BANQUO.)

MACBETH

Avaunt! and quit my sight! let the earth hide thee!

Thy bones are marrowless, thy blood is cold;
Thou hast no speculation in those eyes
Which thou dost glare with!

LADY MACBETH

Think of this, good peers,
But as a thing of custom: 'tis no other;
Only it spoils the pleasure of the time.

MACBETH

What man dare, I dare:
Approach thou like the rugged Russian bear,
The arm'd rhinoceros, or the Hyrcan tiger;
Take any shape but that, and my firm nerves
Shall never tremble: or be alive again,
And dare me to the desert with thy sword;
If trembling I inhabit then, protest me
The baby of a girl. Hence, horrible shadow!
Unreal mockery, hence!

(GHOST OF BANQUO vanishes.)

Why, so: being gone,
I am a man again. Pray you, sit still.

LADY MACBETH

You have displaced the mirth, broke the good meeting,
With most admired disorder.

MACBETH

Can such things be,
And overcome us like a summer's cloud,
Without our special wonder? You make me strange
Even to the disposition that I owe,
When now I think you can behold such sights,
And keep the natural ruby of your cheeks,
When mine is blanched with fear.

ROSS

    What sights, my lord?

LADY MACBETH

    I pray you, speak not; he grows worse and worse;
    Question enrages him. At once, good night:
    Stand not upon the order of your going,
    But go at once.

LENNOX

    Good night; and better health
    Attend his majesty!

LADY MACBETH

    A kind good night to all!

    (Exeunt all but MACBETH and LADY MACBETH.)

MACBETH

    It will have blood; they say, blood will have blood:
    Stones have been known to move and trees to speak;
    Augurs and understood relations have
    By magot-pies and choughs and rooks brought forth
    The secret'st man of blood. What is the night?

LADY MACBETH

    Almost at odds with morning, which is which.

MACBETH

    How say'st thou, that Macduff denies his person
    At our great bidding?

LADY MACBETH

    Did you send to him, sir?

MACBETH

    I hear it by the way; but I will send:
    There's not a one of them but in his house
    I keep a servant fee'd. I will to-morrow,
    And betimes I will, to the weird sisters:
    More shall they speak; for now I am bent to know,
    By the worst means, the worst. For mine own good,
    All causes shall give way: I am in blood
    Stepp'd in so far that, should I wade no more,
    Returning were as tedious as go o'er:
    Strange things I have in head, that will to hand;
    Which must be acted ere they may be scann'd.

LADY MACBETH

    You lack the season of all natures, sleep.

MACBETH

    Come, we'll to sleep. My strange and self-abuse
    Is the initiate fear that wants hard use:
    We are yet but young in deed.

    (Exeunt.)

THE MERCHANT OF VENICE
Act 5, Scene 1
6 Characters: 4 male, 2 female
Gratiano (M), Bassanio (M), Antonio (M), Lorenzo (M), Nerissa (F),
Portia (F)

In the play's final scene, Portia and Nerissa take great relish in casti-
gating Bassanio and Gratiano for giving up their rings to the lawyer
and clerk (impersonated by Portia and Nerissa), knowing that Bassanio and Gratiano have still not guessed the trick.

⟫⟨

Portia's house. A tucket sounds.

LORENZO
> Your husband is at hand; I hear his trumpet:
> We are no tell-tales, madam; fear you not.

PORTIA
> This night methinks is but the daylight sick;
> It looks a little paler: 'tis a day,
> Such as the day is when the sun is hid.

(Enter BASSANIO, ANTONIO, and GRATIANO.)

BASSANIO
> We should hold day with the Antipodes,
> If you would walk in absence of the sun.

PORTIA
> Let me give light, but let me not be light;
> For a light wife doth make a heavy husband,
> And never be Bassanio so for me:
> But God sort all! You are welcome home, my lord.

BASSANIO

I thank you, madam. Give welcome to my friend.
This is the man, this is Antonio,
To whom I am so infinitely bound.

PORTIA

You should in all sense be much bound to him.
For, as I hear, he was much bound for you.

ANTONIO

No more than I am well acquitted of.

PORTIA

Sir, you are very welcome to our house:
It must appear in other ways than words,
Therefore I scant this breathing courtesy.

GRATIANO

(To NERISSA.) By yonder moon I swear you do me wrong;
In faith, I gave it to the judge's clerk:
Would he were gelt that had it, for my part,
Since you do take it, love, so much at heart.

PORTIA

A quarrel, ho, already! what's the matter?

GRATIANO

About a hoop of gold, a paltry ring
That she did give me, whose posy was
For all the world like cutler's poetry
Upon a knife, 'Love me, and leave me not.'

NERISSA

What talk you of the posy or the value?
You swore to me, when I did give it you,
That you would wear it till your hour of death

And that it should lie with you in your grave:
Though not for me, yet for your vehement oaths,
You should have been respective and have kept it.
Gave it a judge's clerk! no, God's my judge,
The clerk will ne'er wear hair on's face that had it.

GRATIANO

He will, an if he live to be a man.

NERISSA

Ay, if a woman live to be a man.

GRATIANO

Now, by this hand, I gave it to a youth,
A kind of boy, a little scrubbed boy,
No higher than thyself; the judge's clerk,
A prating boy, that begg'd it as a fee:
I could not for my heart deny it him.

PORTIA

You were to blame, I must be plain with you,
To part so slightly with your wife's first gift:
A thing stuck on with oaths upon your finger
And so riveted with faith unto your flesh.
I gave my love a ring and made him swear
Never to part with it; and here he stands;
I dare be sworn for him he would not leave it
Nor pluck it from his finger, for the wealth
That the world masters. Now, in faith, Gratiano,
You give your wife too unkind a cause of grief:
An 'twere to me, I should be mad at it.

BASSANIO

(Aside.) Why, I were best to cut my left hand off
And swear I lost the ring defending it.

GRATIANO

> My Lord Bassanio gave his ring away
> Unto the judge that begg'd it and indeed
> Deserved it too; and then the boy, his clerk,
> That took some pains in writing, he begg'd mine;
> And neither man nor master would take aught
> But the two rings.

PORTIA

> What ring gave you my lord?
> Not that, I hope, which you received of me.

BASSANIO

> If I could add a lie unto a fault,
> I would deny it; but you see my finger
> Hath not the ring upon it; it is gone.

PORTIA

> Even so void is your false heart of truth.
> By heaven, I will ne'er come in your bed
> Until I see the ring.

NERISSA

> Nor I in yours
> Till I again see mine.

BASSANIO

> Sweet Portia,
> If you did know to whom I gave the ring,
> If you did know for whom I gave the ring
> And would conceive for what I gave the ring
> And how unwillingly I left the ring,
> When nought would be accepted but the ring,
> You would abate the strength of your displeasure.

PORTIA

> If you had known the virtue of the ring,

Or half her worthiness that gave the ring,
Or your own honour to contain the ring,
You would not then have parted with the ring.
What man is there so much unreasonable,
If you had pleased to have defended it
With any terms of zeal, wanted the modesty
To urge the thing held as a ceremony?
Nerissa teaches me what to believe:
I'll die for't but some woman had the ring.

BASSANIO
No, by my honour, madam, by my soul,
No woman had it, but a civil doctor,
Which did refuse three thousand ducats of me
And begg'd the ring; the which I did deny him
And suffer'd him to go displeased away;
Even he that did uphold the very life
Of my dear friend. What should I say, sweet lady?
I was enforced to send it after him;
I was beset with shame and courtesy;
My honour would not let ingratitude
So much besmear it. Pardon me, good lady;
For, by these blessed candles of the night,
Had you been there, I think you would have begg'd
The ring of me to give the worthy doctor.

PORTIA
Let not that doctor e'er come near my house:
Since he hath got the jewel that I loved,
And that which you did swear to keep for me,
I will become as liberal as you;
I'll not deny him any thing I have,
No, not my body nor my husband's bed:
Know him I shall, I am well sure of it:
Lie not a night from home; watch me like Argus:
If you do not, if I be left alone,

Now, by mine honour, which is yet mine own,
I'll have that doctor for my bedfellow.

NERISSA

And I his clerk; therefore be well advised
How you do leave me to mine own protection.

GRATIANO

Well, do you so; let not me take him, then;
For if I do, I'll mar the young clerk's pen.

ANTONIO

I am the unhappy subject of these quarrels.

PORTIA

Sir, grieve not you; you are welcome notwithstanding.

BASSANIO

Portia, forgive me this enforced wrong;
And, in the hearing of these many friends,
I swear to thee, even by thine own fair eyes,
Wherein I see myself —

PORTIA

Mark you but that!
In both my eyes he doubly sees himself;
In each eye, one: swear by your double self,
And there's an oath of credit.

BASSANIO

Nay, but hear me:
Pardon this fault, and by my soul I swear
I never more will break an oath with thee.

ANTONIO

I once did lend my body for his wealth;

Which, but for him that had your husband's ring,
Had quite miscarried: I dare be bound again,
My soul upon the forfeit, that your lord
Will never more break faith advisedly.

PORTIA

Then you shall be his surety. Give him this
And bid him keep it better than the other.

ANTONIO

Here, Lord Bassanio; swear to keep this ring.

BASSANIO

By heaven, it is the same I gave the doctor!

PORTIA

I had it of him: pardon me, Bassanio;
For, by this ring, the doctor lay with me.

NERISSA

And pardon me, my gentle Gratiano;
For that same scrubbed boy, the doctor's clerk,
In lieu of this last night did lie with me.

GRATIANO

Why, this is like the mending of highways
In summer, where the ways are fair enough:
What, are we cuckolds ere we have deserved it?

PORTIA

Speak not so grossly. You are all amazed:
Here is a letter; read it at your leisure;
It comes from Padua, from Bellario:
There you shall find that Portia was the doctor,
Nerissa there her clerk: Lorenzo here
Shall witness I set forth as soon as you

And even but now return'd; I have not yet
Enter'd my house. Antonio, you are welcome;
And I have better news in store for you
Than you expect: unseal this letter soon;
There you shall find three of your argosies
Are richly come to harbour suddenly:
You shall not know by what strange accident
I chanced on this letter.

ANTONIO

I am dumb.

BASSANIO

Were you the doctor and I knew you not?

GRATIANO

Were you the clerk that is to make me cuckold?

NERISSA

Ay, but the clerk that never means to do it,
Unless he live until he be a man.

BASSANIO

Sweet doctor, you shall be my bed-fellow:
When I am absent, then lie with my wife.

ANTONIO

Sweet lady, you have given me life and living;
For here I read for certain that my ships
Are safely come to road.

PORTIA

How now, Lorenzo!
My clerk hath some good comforts too for you.

NERISSA

Ay, and I'll give them him without a fee.

There do I give to you and Jessica,
From the rich Jew, a special deed of gift,
After his death, of all he dies possess'd of.

LORENZO

Fair ladies, you drop manna in the way
Of starved people.

PORTIA

It is almost morning,
And yet I am sure you are not satisfied
Of these events at full. Let us go in;
And charge us there upon inter'gatories,
And we will answer all things faithfully.

GRATIANO

Let it be so: the first inter'gatory
That my Nerissa shall be sworn on is,
Whether till the next night she had rather stay,
Or go to bed now, being two hours to day:
But were the day come, I should wish it dark,
That I were couching with the doctor's clerk.
Well, while I live I'll fear no other thing
So sore as keeping safe Nerissa's ring.

(Exeunt.)

THE TAMING OF THE SHREW

Act 4, Scene 3
6 Characters: 5 male, 1 female
Grumio (M), Petruchio (M), Hortensio (M), Haberdasher (M), Tailor (M), Katharina (F)

To break Katharina's independent will, Petruchio has been starving her and keeping her sleepless. Katherina begs the servant Grumio to give her some food, but he stalls until Petruchio and Hortensio enter with meat. As she begins to eat, Petruchio distracts her with a new dress and hat, both of which he then denies her by saying they are not good enough.

———➤-●-◄———

*A room in Petruchio's house. Enter KATHARINA and
GRUMIO.*

GRUMIO

No, no, forsooth; I dare not for my life.

KATHARINA

The more my wrong, the more his spite appears:
What, did he marry me to famish me?
Beggars, that come unto my father's door,
Upon entreaty have a present aims;
If not, elsewhere they meet with charity:
But I, who never knew how to entreat,
Nor never needed that I should entreat,
Am starved for meat, giddy for lack of sleep,
With oath kept waking and with brawling fed:
And that which spites me more than all these wants,
He does it under name of perfect love;
As who should say, if I should sleep or eat,
'Twere deadly sickness or else present death.

I prithee go and get me some repast;
I care not what, so it be wholesome food.

GRUMIO

What say you to a neat's foot?

KATHARINA

'Tis passing good: I prithee let me have it.

GRUMIO

I fear it is too choleric a meat.
How say you to a fat tripe finely broil'd?

KATHARINA

I like it well: good Grumio, fetch it me.

GRUMIO

I cannot tell; I fear 'tis choleric.
What say you to a piece of beef and mustard?

KATHARINA

A dish that I do love to feed upon.

GRUMIO

Ay, but the mustard is too hot a little.

KATHARINA

Why then, the beef, and let the mustard rest.

GRUMIO

Nay then, I will not: you shall have the mustard,
Or else you get no beef of Grumio.

KATHARINA

Then both, or one, or any thing thou wilt.

GRUMIO

    Why then, the mustard without the beef.

KATHARINA

    Go, get thee gone, thou false deluding slave,

    (Beats him.)

    That feed'st me with the very name of meat:
    Sorrow on thee and all the pack of you,
    That triumph thus upon my misery!
    Go, get thee gone, I say.

    (Enter PETRUCHIO and HORTENSIO with meat.)

PETRUCHIO

    How fares my Kate? What, sweeting, all amort?

HORTENSIO

    Mistress, what cheer?

KATHARINA

    Faith, as cold as can be.

PETRUCHIO

    Pluck up thy spirits; look cheerfully upon me.
    Here love; thou see'st how diligent I am
    To dress thy meat myself and bring it thee:
    I am sure, sweet Kate, this kindness merits thanks.
    What, not a word? Nay, then thou lovest it not;
    And all my pains is sorted to no proof.
    Here, take away this dish.

KATHARINA

    I pray you, let it stand.

PETRUCHIO

The poorest service is repaid with thanks;
And so shall mine, before you touch the meat.

KATHARINA

I thank you, sir.

HORTENSIO

Signior Petruchio, fie! you are to blame.
Come, mistress Kate, I'll bear you company.

PETRUCHIO

(Aside.) Eat it up all, Hortensio, if thou lovest me.
Much good do it unto thy gentle heart!
Kate, eat apace: and now, my honey love,
Will we return unto thy father's house
And revel it as bravely as the best,
With silken coats and caps and golden rings,
With ruffs and cuffs and fardingales and things;
With scarfs and fans and double change of bravery,
With amber bracelets, beads and all this knavery.
What, hast thou dined? The tailor stays thy leisure,
To deck thy body with his ruffling treasure.

(Enter TAILOR.)

Come, tailor, let us see these ornaments;
Lay forth the gown.

(Enter HABERDASHER.)

What news with you, sir?

HABERDASHER

Here is the cap your worship did bespeak.

PETRUCHIO

> Why, this was moulded on a porringer;
> A velvet dish: fie, fie! 'tis lewd and filthy:
> Why, 'tis a cockle or a walnut-shell,
> A knack, a toy, a trick, a baby's cap:
> Away with it! come, let me have a bigger.

KATHARINA

> I'll have no bigger: this doth fit the time,
> And gentlewomen wear such caps as these

PETRUCHIO

> When you are gentle, you shall have one too,
> And not till then.

HORTENSIO

> (*Aside.*) That will not be in haste.

KATHARINA

> Why, sir, I trust I may have leave to speak;
> And speak I will; I am no child, no babe:
> Your betters have endured me say my mind,
> And if you cannot, best you stop your ears.
> My tongue will tell the anger of my heart,
> Or else my heart concealing it will break,
> And rather than it shall, I will be free
> Even to the uttermost, as I please, in words.

PETRUCHIO

> Why, thou say'st true; it is a paltry cap,
> A custard-coffin, a bauble, a silken pie:
> I love thee well, in that thou likest it not.

KATHARINA

> Love me or love me not, I like the cap;
> And it I will have, or I will have none.

(Exit HABERDASHER.)

PETRUCHIO

Thy gown? why, ay: come, tailor, let us see't.
O mercy, God! what masquing stuff is here?
What's this? a sleeve? 'tis like a demi-cannon:
What, up and down, carved like an apple-tart?
Here's snip and nip and cut and slish and slash,
Like to a censer in a barber's shop:
Why, what, i' devil's name, tailor, call'st thou this?

HORTENSIO

(Aside.) I see she's like to have neither cap nor gown.

TAILOR

You bid me make it orderly and well,
According to the fashion and the time.

PETRUCHIO

Marry, and did; but if you be remember'd,
I did not bid you mar it to the time.
Go, hop me over every kennel home,
For you shall hop without my custom, sir:
I'll none of it: hence! make your best of it.

KATHARINA

I never saw a better-fashion'd gown,
More quaint, more pleasing, nor more commendable:
Belike you mean to make a puppet of me.

PETRUCHIO

Why, true; he means to make a puppet of thee.

TAILOR

She says your worship means to make
a puppet of her.

PETRUCHIO

O monstrous arrogance! Thou liest, thou thread,
thou thimble,
Thou yard, three-quarters, half-yard, quarter, nail!
Thou flea, thou nit, thou winter-cricket thou!
Braved in mine own house with a skein of thread?
Away, thou rag, thou quantity, thou remnant;
Or I shall so be-mete thee with thy yard
As thou shalt think on prating whilst thou livest!
I tell thee, I, that thou hast marr'd her gown.

TAILOR

Your worship is deceived; the gown is made
Just as my master had direction:
Grumio gave order how it should be done.

GRUMIO

I gave him no order; I gave him the stuff.

TAILOR

But how did you desire it should be made?

GRUMIO

Marry, sir, with needle and thread.

TAILOR

But did you not request to have it cut?

GRUMIO

Thou hast faced many things.

TAILOR

I have.

GRUMIO

Face not me: thou hast braved many men; brave not

me; I will neither be faced nor braved. I say unto thee, I bid thy master cut out the gown; but I did not bid him cut it to pieces: ergo, thou liest.

TAILOR
Why, here is the note of the fashion to testify

PETRUCHIO
Read it.

GRUMIO
The note lies in's throat, if he say I said so.

TAILOR
(Reads.) 'Imprimis, a loose-bodied gown:'

GRUMIO
Master, if ever I said loose-bodied gown, sew me in the skirts of it, and beat me to death with a bottom of brown thread: I said a gown.

PETRUCHIO
Proceed.

TAILOR
(Reads.) 'With a small compassed cape:'

GRUMIO
I confess the cape.

TAILOR
(Reads.) 'With a trunk sleeve:'

GRUMIO
I confess two sleeves.

TAILOR

(Reads.) 'The sleeves curiously cut.'

PETRUCHIO

Ay, there's the villany.

GRUMIO

Error i' the bill, sir; error i' the bill.
I commanded the sleeves should be cut out and
sewed up again; and that I'll prove upon thee,
though thy little finger be armed in a thimble.

TAILOR

This is true that I say: an I had thee
in place where, thou shouldst know it.

GRUMIO

I am for thee straight: take thou the
bill, give me thy mete-yard, and spare not me.

HORTENSIO

God-a-mercy, Grumio! then he shall have no odds.

PETRUCHIO

Well, sir, in brief, the gown is not for me.

GRUMIO

You are i' the right, sir: 'tis for my mistress.

PETRUCHIO

Go, take it up unto thy master's use.

GRUMIO

Villain, not for thy life: take up my mistress'
gown for thy master's use!

PETRUCHIO

    Why, sir, what's your conceit in that?

GRUMIO

    O, sir, the conceit is deeper than you think for:
    Take up my mistress' gown to his master's use!
    O, fie, fie, fie!

PETRUCHIO

    (Aside.) Hortensio, say thou wilt see the tailor paid.
    Go take it hence; be gone, and say no more.

HORTENSIO

    Tailor, I'll pay thee for thy gown tomorrow:
    Take no unkindness of his hasty words:
    Away! I say; commend me to thy master.

    (Exit TAILOR.)

A MIDSUMMER NIGHT'S DREAM

Act 3, Scene 1

7 Characters: 6 male, 1 female

Bottom (M), Quince (M), Snug (M), Flute (M), Snout (M), Starveling (M), Puck (F)

The Rude Mechanicals meet for their second rehearsal. Puck, the fairy, infiltrates the gathering and begins to work magical mischief, changing Bottom's head into that of an ass.

———◆———

The wood. TITANIA lying asleep. Enter QUINCE, SNUG, BOTTOM, FLUTE, SNOUT, and STARVELING.

BOTTOM
> Are we all met?

QUINCE
> Pat, pat; and here's a marvellous convenient place
> for our rehearsal. This green plot shall be our
> stage, this hawthorn-brake our tiring-house; and we
> will do it in action as we will do it before the duke.

BOTTOM
> Peter Quince, —

QUINCE
> What sayest thou, bully Bottom?

BOTTOM
> There are things in this comedy of Pyramus and
> Thisbe that will never please. First, Pyramus must
> draw a sword to kill himself; which the ladies
> cannot abide. How answer you that?

SNOUT

By'r lakin, a parlous fear.

STARVELING

I believe we must leave the killing out, when all is done.

BOTTOM

Not a whit: I have a device to make all well.
Write me a prologue; and let the prologue seem to
say, we will do no harm with our swords, and that
Pyramus is not killed indeed; and, for the more
better assurance, tell them that I, Pyramus, am not
Pyramus, but Bottom the weaver: this will put them
out of fear.

QUINCE

Well, we will have such a prologue; and it shall be
written in eight and six.

BOTTOM

No, make it two more; let it be written in eight and eight.

SNOUT

Will not the ladies be afeard of the lion?

STARVELING

I fear it, I promise you.

BOTTOM

Masters, you ought to consider with yourselves: to
bring in — God shield us! — a lion among ladies, is a
most dreadful thing; for there is not a more fearful
wild-fowl than your lion living; and we ought to
look to 't.

SNOUT

Therefore another prologue must tell he is not a lion.

BOTTOM

Nay, you must name his name, and half his face must
be seen through the lion's neck: and he himself
must speak through, saying thus, or to the same
defect, — 'Ladies,' — or 'Fair-ladies — I would wish
You,' — or 'I would request you,' — or 'I would
entreat you, — not to fear, not to tremble: my life
for yours. If you think I come hither as a lion, it
were pity of my life: no I am no such thing; I am a
man as other men are;' and there indeed let him name
his name, and tell them plainly he is Snug the joiner.

QUINCE

Well it shall be so. But there is two hard things;
that is, to bring the moonlight into a chamber; for,
you know, Pyramus and Thisbe meet by moonlight.

SNOUT

Doth the moon shine that night we play our play?

BOTTOM

A calendar, a calendar! look in the almanac; find
out moonshine, find out moonshine.

QUINCE

Yes, it doth shine that night.

BOTTOM

Why, then may you leave a casement of the great
chamber window, where we play, open, and the moon
may shine in at the casement.

QUINCE

Ay; or else one must come in with a bush of thorns
and a lanthorn, and say he comes to disfigure, or to
present, the person of Moonshine. Then, there is

another thing: we must have a wall in the great
chamber; for Pyramus and Thisbe says the story, did
talk through the chink of a wall.

SNOUT

You can never bring in a wall. What say you, Bottom?

BOTTOM

Some man or other must present Wall: and let him
have some plaster, or some loam, or some rough-cast
about him, to signify wall; and let him hold his
fingers thus, and through that cranny shall Pyramus
and Thisbe whisper.

QUINCE

If that may be, then all is well. Come, sit down,
every mother's son, and rehearse your parts.
Pyramus, you begin: when you have spoken your
speech, enter into that brake: and so every one
according to his cue.

(Enter PUCK behind.)

PUCK

What hempen home-spuns have we swaggering here,
So near the cradle of the fairy queen?
What, a play toward! I'll be an auditor;
An actor too, perhaps, if I see cause.

QUINCE

Speak, Pyramus. Thisbe, stand forth.

BOTTOM

Thisbe, the flowers of odious savours sweet, —

QUINCE

Odours, odours.

BOTTOM
> — odours savours sweet:
> So hath thy breath, my dearest Thisbe dear.
> But hark, a voice! stay thou but here awhile,
> And by and by I will to thee appear.

> *(Exit.)*

PUCK
> A stranger Pyramus than e'er played here.

> *(Exit.)*

FLUTE
> Must I speak now?

QUINCE
> Ay, marry, must you; for you must understand he goes
> but to see a noise that he heard, and is to come again.

FLUTE
> Most radiant Pyramus, most lily-white of hue,
> Of colour like the red rose on triumphant brier,
> Most brisky juvenal and eke most lovely Jew,
> As true as truest horse that yet would never tire,
> I'll meet thee, Pyramus, at Ninny's tomb.

QUINCE
> 'Ninus' tomb,' man: why, you must not speak that
> yet; that you answer to Pyramus: you speak all your
> part at once, cues and all Pyramus enter: your cue
> is past; it is, 'never tire.'

FLUTE
> O, — As true as truest horse, that yet would
> never tire.

(Re-enter PUCK and BOTTOM with an ass's head.)

BOTTOM

If I were fair, Thisbe, I were only thine.

QUINCE

O monstrous! O strange! we are haunted. Pray, masters! fly, masters! Help!

(Exeunt QUINCE, SNUG, FLUTE, SNOUT, and STARVELING.)

PUCK

I'll follow you, I'll lead you about a round,
Through bog, through bush, through brake, through brier:
Sometime a horse I'll be, sometime a hound,
A hog, a headless bear, sometime a fire;
And neigh, and bark, and grunt, and roar, and burn,
Like horse, hound, hog, bear, fire, at every turn.

(Exit.)

BOTTOM

Why do they run away? this is a knavery of them to make me afeard.

(Re-enter SNOUT.)

SNOUT

O Bottom, thou art changed! what do I see on thee?

BOTTOM

What do you see? you see an asshead of your own, do you?

(Exit SNOUT.)

(Re-enter QUINCE.)

QUINCE

Bless thee, Bottom! bless thee! thou art
translated.

(Exit.)

BOTTOM

I see their knavery: this is to make an ass of me;
to fright me, if they could. But I will not stir
from this place, do what they can: I will walk up
and down here, and I will sing, that they shall hear
I am not afraid.

THE MERRY WIVES OF WINDSOR

Act 3, Scene 4
7 Characters: 4 male, 3 female
Fenton (M), Page (M), Shallow (M), Slender (M), Mistreess Page (F),
Mistress Quickly (F), Anne Page (F)

Slender and Fenton, two suitors for Anne Page, come to press their
courtship.

—————⇒•○•⇐—————

A room in Page's house. Enter FENTON and ANNE PAGE.

FENTON

    I see I cannot get thy father's love;
    Therefore no more turn me to him, sweet Nan.

ANNE PAGE

    Alas, how then?

FENTON

    Why, thou must be thyself.
    He doth object I am too great of birth — ,
    And that, my state being gall'd with my expense,
    I seek to heal it only by his wealth:
    Besides these, other bars he lays before me,
    My riots past, my wild societies;
    And tells me 'tis a thing impossible
    I should love thee but as a property.

ANNE PAGE

    May be he tells you true.

FENTON

    No, heaven so speed me in my time to come!
    Albeit I will confess thy father's wealth
    Was the first motive that I woo'd thee, Anne:

Yet, wooing thee, I found thee of more value
Than stamps in gold or sums in sealed bags;
And 'tis the very riches of thyself
That now I aim at.

ANNE PAGE
Gentle Master Fenton,
Yet seek my father's love; still seek it, sir:
If opportunity and humblest suit
Cannot attain it, why, then, — hark you hither!

(They converse apart.)
(Enter SHALLOW, SLENDER, and MISTRESS QUICKLY.)

SHALLOW
Break their talk, Mistress Quickly: my kinsman shall
speak for himself.

SLENDER
I'll make a shaft or a bolt on't: 'slid, 'tis but
venturing.

SHALLOW
Be not dismayed.

SLENDER
No, she shall not dismay me: I care not for that,
but that I am afeard.

MISTRESS QUICKLY
Hark ye; Master Slender would speak a word with you.

ANNE PAGE
I come to him.
(Aside.) This is my father's choice.
O, what a world of vile ill-favor'd faults
Looks handsome in three hundred pounds a-year!

MISTRESS QUICKLY

And how does good Master Fenton? Pray you, a word with you.

SHALLOW

She's coming; to her, coz. O boy, thou hadst a father!

SLENDER

I had a father, Mistress Anne; my uncle can tell you good jests of him. Pray you, uncle, tell Mistress Anne the jest, how my father stole two geese out of a pen, good uncle.

SHALLOW

Mistress Anne, my cousin loves you.

SLENDER

Ay, that I do; as well as I love any woman in Gloucestershire.

SHALLOW

He will maintain you like a gentlewoman.

SLENDER

Ay, that I will, come cut and long-tail, under the degree of a squire.

SHALLOW

He will make you a hundred and fifty pounds jointure.

ANNE PAGE

Good Master Shallow, let him woo for himself.

SHALLOW

Marry, I thank you for it; I thank you for that good comfort. She calls you, coz: I'll leave you.

ANNE PAGE

Now, Master Slender, —

SLENDER

Now, good Mistress Anne, —

ANNE PAGE

What is your will?

SLENDER

My will! 'od's heartlings, that's a pretty jest
indeed! I ne'er made my will yet, I thank heaven; I
am not such a sickly creature, I give heaven praise.

ANNE PAGE

I mean, Master Slender, what would you with me?

SLENDER

Truly, for mine own part, I would little or nothing
with you. Your father and my uncle hath made
motions: if it be my luck, so; if not, happy man be
his dole! They can tell you how things go better
than I can: you may ask your father; here he comes.

(Enter PAGE and MISTRESS PAGE.)

PAGE

Now, Master Slender: love him, daughter Anne.
Why, how now! what does Master Fenton here?
You wrong me, sir, thus still to haunt my house:
I told you, sir, my daughter is disposed of.

FENTON

Nay, Master Page, be not impatient.

MISTRESS PAGE

Good Master Fenton, come not to my child.

PAGE

She is no match for you.

FENTON

    Sir, will you hear me?

PAGE

    No, good Master Fenton.

    Come, Master Shallow; come, son Slender, in.

    Knowing my mind, you wrong me, Master Fenton.

    (Exeunt PAGE, SHALLOW, and SLENDER.)

MISTRESS QUICKLY

    Speak to Mistress Page.

FENTON

    Good Mistress Page, for that I love your daughter

    In such a righteous fashion as I do,

    Perforce, against all cheques, rebukes and manners,

    I must advance the colours of my love

    And not retire: let me have your good will.

ANNE PAGE

    Good mother, do not marry me to yond fool.

MISTRESS PAGE

    I mean it not; I seek you a better husband.

MISTRESS QUICKLY

    That's my master, master doctor.

ANNE PAGE

    Alas, I had rather be set quick i' the earth

    And bowl'd to death with turnips!

MISTRESS PAGE

    Come, trouble not yourself. Good Master Fenton,

    I will not be your friend nor enemy:

    My daughter will I question how she loves you,

    And as I find her, so am I affected.

Till then farewell, sir: she must needs go in;
Her father will be angry.

FENTON

Farewell, gentle mistress: farewell, Nan.

(Exeunt MISTRESS PAGE and ANNE PAGE.)

MISTRESS QUICKLY

This is my doing, now: 'Nay,' said I, 'will you cast
away your child on a fool, and a physician? Look on
Master Fenton:' this is my doing.

FENTON

I thank thee; and I pray thee, once to-night
Give my sweet Nan this ring: there's for thy pains.

MISTRESS QUICKLY

Now heaven send thee good fortune!

(Exit FENTON.)

A kind heart he hath: a woman would run through
fire and water for such a kind heart. But yet I
would my master had Mistress Anne; or I would
Master Slender had her; or, in sooth, I would Master
Fenton had her; I will do what I can for them all
three; for so I have promised, and I'll be as good
as my word; but speciously for Master Fenton. Well,
I must of another errand to Sir John Falstaff from
my two mistresses: what a beast am I to slack it!

(Exit.)

HAMLET

Act 3, Scene 2

8 Characters: 5 male, 3 female

Hamlet (M), Ophelia (F), King (M), Gertrude (F), Player King (M), Player Queen (F), Lucianus (M), Polonius (M)

With the entire court in attendance, The Players perform the short play Hamlet has written that intimates the King has conspired with Gertrude to kill Hamlet's father. At the climax, the King is so upset, he shouts out to end the play, convincing Hamlet of his guilt.

———————————

A hall in the castle.

HAMLET
   Is this a prologue, or the posy of a ring?

OPHELIA
   'Tis brief, my lord.

HAMLET
   As woman's love.

   (Enter two PLAYERS, King and Queen.)

PLAYER KING
   Full thirty times hath Phoebus' cart gone round
   Neptune's salt wash and Tellus' orbed ground,
   And thirty dozen moons with borrow'd sheen
   About the world have times twelve thirties been,
   Since love our hearts and Hymen did our hands
   Unite commutual in most sacred bands.

PLAYER QUEEN
   So many journeys may the sun and moon

Make us again count o'er ere love be done!
But, woe is me, you are so sick of late,
So far from cheer and from your former state,
That I distrust you. Yet, though I distrust,
Discomfort you, my lord, it nothing must:
For women's fear and love holds quantity;
In neither aught, or in extremity.
Now, what my love is, proof hath made you know;
And as my love is sized, my fear is so:
Where love is great, the littlest doubts are fear;
Where little fears grow great, great love grows there.

PLAYER KING
'Faith, I must leave thee, love, and shortly too;
My operant powers their functions leave to do:
And thou shalt live in this fair world behind,
Honour'd, beloved; and haply one as kind
For husband shalt thou —

PLAYER QUEEN
O, confound the rest!
Such love must needs be treason in my breast:
In second husband let me be accurst!
None wed the second but who kill'd the first.

HAMLET
(Aside.) Wormwood, wormwood.

PLAYER QUEEN
The instances that second marriage move
Are base respects of thrift, but none of love:
A second time I kill my husband dead,
When second husband kisses me in bed.

PLAYER KING
I do believe you think what now you speak;

But what we do determine oft we break.
Purpose is but the slave to memory,
Of violent birth, but poor validity;
Which now, like fruit unripe, sticks on the tree;
But fall, unshaken, when they mellow be.
Most necessary 'tis that we forget
To pay ourselves what to ourselves is debt:
What to ourselves in passion we propose,
The passion ending, doth the purpose lose.
The violence of either grief or joy
Their own enactures with themselves destroy:
Where joy most revels, grief doth most lament;
Grief joys, joy grieves, on slender accident.
This world is not for aye, nor 'tis not strange
That even our loves should with our fortunes change;
For 'tis a question left us yet to prove,
Whether love lead fortune, or else fortune love.
The great man down, you mark his favourite flies;
The poor advanced makes friends of enemies.
And hitherto doth love on fortune tend;
For who not needs shall never lack a friend,
And who in want a hollow friend doth try,
Directly seasons him his enemy.
But, orderly to end where I begun,
Our wills and fates do so contrary run
That our devices still are overthrown;
Our thoughts are ours, their ends none of our own:
So think thou wilt no second husband wed;
But die thy thoughts when thy first lord is dead.

PLAYER QUEEN
Nor earth to me give food, nor heaven light!
Sport and repose lock from me day and night!
To desperation turn my trust and hope!
An anchor's cheer in prison be my scope!
Each opposite that blanks the face of joy

Meet what I would have well and it destroy!
Both here and hence pursue me lasting strife,
If, once a widow, ever I be wife!

HAMLET
If she should break it now!

PLAYER KING

'Tis deeply sworn. Sweet, leave me here awhile;
My spirits grow dull, and fain I would beguile
The tedious day with sleep.

(Sleeps.)

PLAYER QUEEN
Sleep rock thy brain,
And never come mischance between us twain!

(Exit.)

HAMLET
Madam, how like you this play?

QUEEN GERTRUDE
The lady protests too much, methinks.

HAMLET
O, but she'll keep her word.

KING CLAUDIUS
Have you heard the argument? Is there no offence in 't?

HAMLET
No, no, they do but jest, poison in jest; no offence
i' the world.

KING CLAUDIUS

What do you call the play?

HAMLET

The Mouse-trap. Marry, how? Tropically. This play
is the image of a murder done in Vienna: Gonzago is
the duke's name; his wife, Baptista: you shall see
anon; 'tis a knavish piece of work: but what o'
that? your majesty and we that have free souls, it
touches us not: let the galled jade wince, our
withers are unwrung.

(Enter LUCIANUS.)

This is one Lucianus, nephew to the king.

OPHELIA

You are as good as a chorus, my lord.

HAMLET

I could interpret between you and your love, if I
could see the puppets dallying.

OPHELIA

You are keen, my lord, you are keen.

HAMLET

It would cost you a groaning to take off my edge.

OPHELIA

Still better, and worse.

HAMLET

So you must take your husbands. Begin, murderer;
pox, leave thy damnable faces, and begin. Come:
'the croaking raven doth bellow for revenge.'

LUCIANUS
>Thoughts black, hands apt, drugs fit, and time agreeing;
>Confederate season, else no creature seeing;
>Thou mixture rank, of midnight weeds collected,
>With Hecate's ban thrice blasted, thrice infected,
>Thy natural magic and dire property,
>On wholesome life usurp immediately.

(Pours the poison into the sleeper's ears.)

HAMLET
>He poisons him i' the garden for's estate. His
>name's Gonzago: the story is extant, and writ in
>choice Italian: you shall see anon how the murderer
>gets the love of Gonzago's wife.

OPHELIA
>The king rises.

HAMLET
>What, frighted with false fire!

QUEEN GERTRUDE
>How fares my lord?

LORD POLONIUS
>Give o'er the play.

KING CLAUDIUS
>Give me some light: away!

POLONIUS:
>Lights, lights, lights!

MUCH ADO ABOUT NOTHING

Act 4, Scene 1

8 Characters: 7 male, 1 female

Leonato (M), Friar Francis (M), Claudio (M), Hero (M), Don
Pedro (M), Benedick (M), Don John (M), Beatrice (F)

As Hero and Claudio stand at the altar about to be married, Claudio suddenly accuses her of being unfaithful. At first, Hero's father,
Leonato, believes him, and Hero faints. Claudio and his friends leave
the church.

———»·o·«———

*A church. Enter DON PEDRO, DON JOHN, LEONATO,
FRIAR FRANCIS, CLAUDIO, BENEDICK, HERO, BEAT-
RICE, and ATTENDANTS.*

LEONATO
Come, Friar Francis, be brief; only to the plain
form of marriage, and you shall recount their
particular duties afterwards.

FRIAR FRANCIS
You come hither, my lord, to marry this lady.

CLAUDIO
No.

LEONATO
To be married to her: friar, you come to marry her.

FRIAR FRANCIS
Lady, you come hither to be married to this count.

HERO
I do.

FRIAR FRANCIS
    If either of you know any inward impediment why you
    should not be conjoined, charge you, on your souls,
    to utter it.

CLAUDIO
    Know you any, Hero?

HERO
    None, my lord.

FRIAR FRANCIS
    Know you any, count?

LEONATO
    I dare make his answer, none.

CLAUDIO
    O, what men dare do! what men may do! what men daily
    do, not knowing what they do!

BENEDICK
    How now! interjections? Why, then, some be of
    laughing, as, ah, ha, he!

CLAUDIO
    Stand thee by, friar. Father, by your leave:
    Will you with free and unconstrained soul
    Give me this maid, your daughter?

LEONATO
    As freely, son, as God did give her me.

CLAUDIO
    And what have I to give you back, whose worth
    May counterpoise this rich and precious gift?

DON PEDRO
    Nothing, unless you render her again.

CLAUDIO

Sweet prince, you learn me noble thankfulness.
There, Leonato, take her back again:
Give not this rotten orange to your friend;
She's but the sign and semblance of her honour.
Behold how like a maid she blushes here!
O, what authority and show of truth
Can cunning sin cover itself withal!
Comes not that blood as modest evidence
To witness simple virtue? Would you not swear,
All you that see her, that she were a maid,
By these exterior shows? But she is none:
She knows the heat of a luxurious bed;
Her blush is guiltiness, not modesty.

LEONATO

What do you mean, my lord?

CLAUDIO

Not to be married,
Not to knit my soul to an approved wanton.

LEONATO

Dear my lord, if you, in your own proof,
Have vanquish'd the resistance of her youth,
And made defeat of her virginity, —

CLAUDIO

I know what you would say: if I have known her,
You will say she did embrace me as a husband,
And so extenuate the 'forehand sin:
No, Leonato,
I never tempted her with word too large;
But, as a brother to his sister, show'd
Bashful sincerity and comely love.

HERO

And seem'd I ever otherwise to you?

CLAUDIO

Out on thee! Seeming! I will write against it:
You seem to me as Dian in her orb,
As chaste as is the bud ere it be blown;
But you are more intemperate in your blood
Than Venus, or those pamper'd animals
That rage in savage sensuality.

HERO

Is my lord well, that he doth speak so wide?

LEONATO

Sweet prince, why speak not you?

DON PEDRO

What should I speak?
I stand dishonour'd, that have gone about
To link my dear friend to a common stale.

LEONATO

Are these things spoken, or do I but dream?

DON JOHN

Sir, they are spoken, and these things are true.

BENEDICK

This looks not like a nuptial.

HERO

True! O God!

CLAUDIO

Leonato, stand I here?
Is this the prince? is this the prince's brother?
Is this face Hero's? are our eyes our own?

LEONATO

All this is so: but what of this, my lord?

CLAUDIO

Let me but move one question to your daughter;
And, by that fatherly and kindly power
That you have in her, bid her answer truly.

LEONATO

I charge thee do so, as thou art my child.

HERO

O, God defend me! how am I beset!
What kind of catechising call you this?

CLAUDIO

To make you answer truly to your name.

HERO

Is it not Hero? Who can blot that name
With any just reproach?

CLAUDIO

Marry, that can Hero;
Hero itself can blot out Hero's virtue.
What man was he talk'd with you yesternight
Out at your window betwixt twelve and one?
Now, if you are a maid, answer to this.

HERO

I talk'd with no man at that hour, my lord.

DON PEDRO

Why, then are you no maiden. Leonato,
I am sorry you must hear: upon mine honour,
Myself, my brother and this grieved count
Did see her, hear her, at that hour last night
Talk with a ruffian at her chamber-window
Who hath indeed, most like a liberal villain,
Confess'd the vile encounters they have had
A thousand times in secret.

DON JOHN

    Fie, fie! they are not to be named, my lord,
    Not to be spoke of;
    There is not chastity enough in language
    Without offence to utter them. Thus, pretty lady,
    I am sorry for thy much misgovernment.

CLAUDIO

    O Hero, what a Hero hadst thou been,
    If half thy outward graces had been placed
    About thy thoughts and counsels of thy heart!
    But fare thee well, most foul, most fair! farewell,
    Thou pure impiety and impious purity!
    For thee I'll lock up all the gates of love,
    And on my eyelids shall conjecture hang,
    To turn all beauty into thoughts of harm,
    And never shall it more be gracious.

LEONATO

    Hath no man's dagger here a point for me?

(HERO swoons.)

BEATRICE

    Why, how now, cousin! wherefore sink you down?

DON JOHN

    Come, let us go. These things, come thus to light,
    Smother her spirits up.

(Exeunt DON PEDRO, DON JOHN, and CLAUDIO.)

A MIDSUMMER NIGHT'S DREAM

Act 5, Scene 1

12 Characters: 9 male, 3 female

Bottom-Pyramus (M), Flute-Thisbe (M), Snout-Wall (M),
Starveling-Moonshine (M), Snug-Lion (M), Quince-Prologue (M),
Theseus (M), Lysander (M), Demetrius (M), Hippolyta (F), Hermia (F),
Helena (F)

The Rude Mechanicals perform their play for the Duke and Duchess,
Theseus and Hippolyta. It is a comic disaster.

➤●◄

Athens. The palace of Theseus. Enter QUINCE for the Prologue.

Prologue:
    If we offend, it is with our good will.
    That you should think, we come not to offend,
    But with good will. To show our simple skill,
    That is the true beginning of our end.
    Consider then we come but in despite.
    We do not come as minding to contest you,
    Our true intent is. All for your delight
    We are not here. That you should here repent you,
    The actors are at hand and by their show
    You shall know all that you are like to know.

THESEUS
    This fellow doth not stand upon points.

LYSANDER
    He hath rid his prologue like a rough colt; he knows
    not the stop. A good moral, my lord: it is not
    enough to speak, but to speak true.

HIPPOLYTA

> Indeed he hath played on his prologue like a child
> on a recorder; a sound, but not in government.

THESEUS

> His speech, was like a tangled chain; nothing
> impaired, but all disordered. Who is next?

> *(Enter PYRAMUS, THISBE, WALL, MOONSHINE, and
> LION.)*

Prologue:

> Gentles, perchance you wonder at this show;
> But wonder on, till truth make all things plain.
> This man is Pyramus, if you would know;
> This beauteous lady Thisbe is certain.
> This man, with lime and rough-cast, doth present
> Wall, that vile Wall which did these lovers sunder;
> And through Wall's chink, poor souls, they are content
> To whisper. At the which let no man wonder.
> This man, with lanthorn, dog, and bush of thorn,
> Presenteth Moonshine; for, if you will know,
> By moonshine did these lovers think no scorn
> To meet at Ninus' tomb, there, there to woo.
> This grisly beast, which Lion hight by name,
> The trusty Thisbe, coming first by night,
> Did scare away, or rather did affright;
> And, as she fled, her mantle she did fall,
> Which Lion vile with bloody mouth did stain.
> Anon comes Pyramus, sweet youth and tall,
> And finds his trusty Thisbe's mantle slain:
> Whereat, with blade, with bloody blameful blade,
> He bravely broach'd is boiling bloody breast;
> And Thisbe, tarrying in mulberry shade,
> His dagger drew, and died. For all the rest,
> Let Lion, Moonshine, Wall, and lovers twain
> At large discourse, while here they do remain.

(Exeunt QUINCE, THISBE, LION, and MOONSHINE.)

THESEUS

I wonder if the lion be to speak.

DEMETRIUS

No wonder, my lord: one lion may, when many asses do.

WALL

In this same interlude it doth befall
That I, one Snout by name, present a wall;
And such a wall, as I would have you think,
That had in it a crannied hole or chink,
Through which the lovers, Pyramus and Thisbe,
Did whisper often very secretly.
This loam, this rough-cast and this stone doth show
That I am that same wall; the truth is so:
And this the cranny is, right and sinister,
Through which the fearful lovers are to whisper.

THESEUS

Would you desire lime and hair to speak better?

DEMETRIUS

It is the wittiest partition that ever I heard
discourse, my lord.

(Enter PYRAMUS.)

THESEUS

Pyramus draws near the wall: silence!

PYRAMUS

O grim-look'd night! O night with hue so black!
O night, which ever art when day is not!
O night, O night! alack, alack, alack,

I fear my Thisbe's promise is forgot!
And thou, O wall, O sweet, O lovely wall,
That stand'st between her father's ground and mine!
Thou wall, O wall, O sweet and lovely wall,
Show me thy chink, to blink through with mine eyne!

(WALL holds up his fingers.)

Thanks, courteous wall: Jove shield thee well for this!
But what see I? No Thisbe do I see.
O wicked wall, through whom I see no bliss!
Cursed be thy stones for thus deceiving me!

THESEUS
    The wall, methinks, being sensible, should curse again.

PYRAMUS
    No, in truth, sir, he should not. 'Deceiving me'
    is Thisbe's cue: she is to enter now, and I am to
    spy her through the wall. You shall see, it will
    fall pat as I told you. Yonder she comes.

(Enter THISBE.)

THISBE
    O wall, full often hast thou heard my moans,
    For parting my fair Pyramus and me!
    My cherry lips have often kiss'd thy stones,
    Thy stones with lime and hair knit up in thee.

PYRAMUS
    I see a voice: now will I to the chink,
    To spy an I can hear my Thisbe's face. Thisbe!

THISBE
    My love thou art, my love I think.

PYRAMUS

Think what thou wilt, I am thy lover's grace;
And, like Limander, am I trusty still.

THISBE

And I like Helen, till the Fates me kill.

PYRAMUS

Not Shafalus to Procrus was so true.

THISBE

As Shafalus to Procrus, I to you.

PYRAMUS

O kiss me through the hole of this vile wall!

THISBE

I kiss the wall's hole, not your lips at all.

PYRAMUS

Wilt thou at Ninny's tomb meet me straightway?

THISBE

'Tide life, 'tide death, I come without delay.

(Exeunt PYRAMUS and THISBE.)

WALL

Thus have I, Wall, my part discharged so;
And, being done, thus Wall away doth go.

(Exit.)

THESEUS

Now is the mural down between the two neighbours.

DEMETRIUS
No remedy, my lord, when walls are so wilful to hear without warning.

HIPPOLYTA
This is the silliest stuff that ever I heard.

THESEUS
The best in this kind are but shadows; and the worst are no worse, if imagination amend them.

HIPPOLYTA
It must be your imagination then, and not theirs.

THESEUS
If we imagine no worse of them than they of themselves, they may pass for excellent men. Here come two noble beasts in, a man and a lion.

(Enter LION and MOONSHINE.)

LION
You, ladies, you, whose gentle hearts do fear
The smallest monstrous mouse that creeps on floor,
May now perchance both quake and tremble here,
When lion rough in wildest rage doth roar.
Then know that I, one Snug the joiner, am
A lion-fell, nor else no lion's dam;
For, if I should as lion come in strife
Into this place, 'twere pity on my life.

THESEUS
A very gentle beast, of a good conscience.

DEMETRIUS
The very best at a beast, my lord, that e'er I saw.

LYSANDER

    This lion is a very fox for his valour.

THESEUS

    True; and a goose for his discretion.

DEMETRIUS

    Not so, my lord; for his valour cannot carry his
    discretion; and the fox carries the goose.

THESEUS

    His discretion, I am sure, cannot carry his valour;
    for the goose carries not the fox. It is well:
    leave it to his discretion, and let us listen to the moon.

MOONSHINE

    This lanthorn doth the horned moon present; —

DEMETRIUS

    He should have worn the horns on his head.

THESEUS

    He is no crescent, and his horns are
    invisible within the circumference.

MOONSHINE

    This lanthorn doth the horned moon present;
    Myself the man i' the moon do seem to be.

THESEUS

    This is the greatest error of all the rest: the man
    should be put into the lanthorn. How is it else the
    man i' the moon?

DEMETRIUS

    He dares not come there for the candle; for, you
    see, it is already in snuff.

HIPPOLYTA

I am aweary of this moon: would he would change!

THESEUS

It appears, by his small light of discretion, that
he is in the wane; but yet, in courtesy, in all
reason, we must stay the time.

LYSANDER

Proceed, Moon.

MOONSHINE

All that I have to say, is, to tell you that the
lanthorn is the moon; I, the man in the moon; this
thorn-bush, my thorn-bush; and this dog, my dog.

DEMETRIUS

Why, all these should be in the lanthorn; for all
these are in the moon. But, silence! here comes Thisbe.

(Enter THISBE.)

THISBE

This is old Ninny's tomb. Where is my love?

LION

(Roaring.) Oh —

(THISBE runs off.)

DEMETRIUS

Well roared, Lion.

THESEUS

Well run, Thisbe.

HIPPOLYTA
> Well shone, Moon. Truly, the moon shines with a
> good grace.

(The LION shakes THISBE'S mantle, and exit.)

THESEUS
> Well moused, Lion.

LYSANDER
> And so the lion vanished.

DEMETRIUS
> And then came Pyramus.

(Enter PYRAMUS.)

PYRAMUS
> Sweet Moon, I thank thee for thy sunny beams;
> I thank thee, Moon, for shining now so bright;
> For, by thy gracious, golden, glittering gleams,
> I trust to take of truest Thisbe sight.
> But stay, O spite!
> But mark, poor knight,
> What dreadful dole is here!
> Eyes, do you see?
> How can it be?
> O dainty duck! O dear!
> Thy mantle good,
> What, stain'd with blood!
> Approach, ye Furies fell!
> O Fates, come, come,
> Cut thread and thrum;
> Quail, crush, conclude, and quell!

THESEUS
> This passion, and the death of a dear friend, would
> go near to make a man look sad.

HIPPOLYTA
> Beshrew my heart, but I pity the man.

PYRAMUS
> O wherefore, Nature, didst thou lions frame?
> Since lion vile hath here deflower'd my dear:
> Which is — no, no — which was the fairest dame
> That lived, that loved, that liked, that look'd
> with cheer.
> Come, tears, confound;
> Out, sword, and wound
> The pap of Pyramus;
> Ay, that left pap,
> Where heart doth hop:
>
> *(Stabs himself.)*
>
> Thus die I, thus, thus, thus.
> Now am I dead,
> Now am I fled;
> My soul is in the sky:
> Tongue, lose thy light;
> Moon take thy flight:
>
> *(Exit MOONSHINE.)*
>
> Now die, die, die, die, die.
>
> *(Dies.)*

DEMETRIUS
> No die, but an ace, for him; for he is but one.

LYSANDER

Less than an ace, man; for he is dead; he is nothing.

THESEUS

With the help of a surgeon he might yet recover, and prove an ass.

HIPPOLYTA

How chance Moonshine is gone before Thisbe comes back and finds her lover?

THESEUS

She will find him by starlight. Here she comes; and her passion ends the play.

(Re-enter THISBE.)

HIPPOLYTA

Methinks she should not use a long one for such a Pyramus: I hope she will be brief.

DEMETRIUS

A mote will turn the balance, which Pyramus, which Thisbe, is the better; he for a man, God warrant us; she for a woman, God bless us.

LYSANDER

She hath spied him already with those sweet eyes.

DEMETRIUS

And thus she means, videlicet: —

THISBE

Asleep, my love?
What, dead, my dove?
O Pyramus, arise!

Speak, speak. Quite dumb?
Dead, dead? A tomb
Must cover thy sweet eyes.
These My lips,
This cherry nose,
These yellow cowslip cheeks,
Are gone, are gone:
Lovers, make moan:
His eyes were green as leeks.
O Sisters Three,
Come, come to me,
With hands as pale as milk;
Lay them in gore,
Since you have shore
With shears his thread of silk.
Tongue, not a word:
Come, trusty sword;
Come, blade, my breast imbrue:

(Stabs herself.)

And, farewell, friends;
Thus Thisbe ends:
Adieu, adieu, adieu.

(Dies.)

THESEUS
Moonshine and Lion are left to bury the dead.

DEMETRIUS
Ay, and Wall too.

BOTTOM
(Starting up.) No assure you; the wall is down that
parted their fathers. Will it please you to see the

epilogue, or to hear a Bergomask dance between two
of our company?

THESEUS

No epilogue, I pray you; for your play needs no
excuse. Never excuse; for when the players are all
dead, there needs none to be blamed. Marry, if he
that writ it had played Pyramus and hanged himself
in Thisbe's garter, it would have been a fine
tragedy: and so it is, truly; and very notably
discharged. But come, your Bergomask: let your
epilogue alone.

RICHARD III

Act 5, Scene 3

13 Characters: 2 male, 1 female, 10 male or female

Richard (M), his enemy Richmond (M), the ghosts of 11 of Richard's victims (Lady Anne (F), Prince (M/F), Edward (M/F), Henry VI (M/F), Clarence (M/F), Rivers (M/F), Grey (M/F), Vaughan (M/F), Hastings (M/F), the two young princes (M/F), Buckingham (M/F)

The night before a battle to retain his kingship, Richard and his enemy, Richmond, are visited by the ghosts of the people Richard has killed to get to be king in the first place. (Though Richard and Richmond are asleep in different tents, they should be placed close enough together so that the ghosts can speak to both of them.)

━━━━━➤●◄━━━━━

Bosworth Field.

RICHMOND

    Good lords, conduct him to his regiment:

    I'll strive, with troubled thoughts, to take a nap,

    Lest leaden slumber peise me down to-morrow,

    When I should mount with wings of victory:

    Once more, good night, kind lords and gentlemen.

(Exeunt all but RICHMOND.)

    O Thou, whose captain I account myself,

    Look on my forces with a gracious eye;

    Put in their hands thy bruising irons of wrath,

    That they may crush down with a heavy fall

    The usurping helmets of our adversaries!

    Make us thy ministers of chastisement,

    That we may praise thee in the victory!

To thee I do commend my watchful soul,
Ere I let fall the windows of mine eyes:
Sleeping and waking, O, defend me still!

(Sleeps.)

(Enter the GHOST OF PRINCE EDWARD, son to King Henry VI.)

GHOST OF PRINCE EDWARD
    (To KING RICHARD III.)
    Let me sit heavy on thy soul to-morrow!
    Think, how thou stab'dst me in my prime of youth
    At Tewksbury: despair, therefore, and die!

    (To RICHMOND.)
    Be cheerful, Richmond; for the wronged souls
    Of butcher'd princes fight in thy behalf
    King Henry's issue, Richmond, comforts thee.

    (Enter the GHOST OF KING HENRY VI.)

GHOST OF KING HENRY VI
    (To KING RICHARD III.)
    When I was mortal, my anointed body
    By thee was punched full of deadly holes
    Think on the Tower and me: despair, and die!
    Harry the Sixth bids thee despair, and die!

    (To RICHMOND.)
    Virtuous and holy, be thou conqueror!
    Harry, that prophesied thou shouldst be king,
    Doth comfort thee in thy sleep: live, and flourish!

(Enter the GHOST OF CLARENCE.)

GHOST OF CLARENCE
   (To KING RICHARD III.)
   Let me sit heavy on thy soul to-morrow!
   I, that was wash'd to death with fulsome wine,
   Poor Clarence, by thy guile betrayed to death!
   To-morrow in the battle think on me,
   And fall thy edgeless sword: despair, and die! —

   (To RICHMOND.)
   Thou offspring of the house of Lancaster
   The wronged heirs of York do pray for thee
   Good angels guard thy battle! live, and flourish!

   (Enter the GHOSTS OF RIVERS, GRAY, and VAUGHAN.)

GHOST OF RIVERS
   (To KING RICHARD III.)
   Let me sit heavy on thy soul tomorrow,
   Rivers, that died at Pomfret! despair, and die!

GHOST OF GREY
   (To KING RICHARD III.)
   Think upon Grey, and let thy soul despair!

GHOST OF VAUGHAN
   (To KING RICHARD III.)
   Think upon Vaughan, and, with guilty fear,
   Let fall thy lance: despair, and die!

ALL
   (To RICHMOND.)
   Awake, and think our wrongs in Richard's bosom
   Will conquer him! awake, and win the day!

   (Enter the GHOST OF HASTINGS.)

GHOST OF HASTINGS
    (To KING RICHARD III.)
    Bloody and guilty, guiltily awake,
    And in a bloody battle end thy days!
    Think on Lord Hastings: despair, and die!

    (To RICHMOND.)
    Quiet untroubled soul, awake, awake!
    Arm, fight, and conquer, for fair England's sake!

    (Enter the GHOSTS OF THE TWO YOUNG PRINCES.)

GHOSTS OF YOUNG PRINCES
    (To KING RICHARD III.)
    Dream on thy cousins smother'd in the Tower:
    Let us be led within thy bosom, Richard,
    And weigh thee down to ruin, shame, and death!
    Thy nephews' souls bid thee despair and die!

    (To RICHMOND.)
    Sleep, Richmond, sleep in peace, and wake in joy;
    Good angels guard thee from the boar's annoy!
    Live, and beget a happy race of kings!
    Edward's unhappy sons do bid thee flourish.

    (Enter the GHOST OF LADY ANNE.)

GHOST OF LADY ANNE
    (To KING RICHARD III.)
    Richard, thy wife, that wretched Anne thy wife,
    That never slept a quiet hour with thee,
    Now fills thy sleep with perturbations
    To-morrow in the battle think on me,
    And fall thy edgeless sword: despair, and die!

(To RICHMOND.)
Thou quiet soul, sleep thou a quiet sleep
Dream of success and happy victory!
Thy adversary's wife doth pray for thee.

(Enter the GHOST OF BUCKINGHAM.)

GHOST OF BUCKINGHAM
  (To KING RICHARD III.)
  The last was I that helped thee to the crown;
  The last was I that felt thy tyranny:
  O, in the battle think on Buckingham,
  And die in terror of thy guiltiness!
  Dream on, dream on, of bloody deeds and death:
  Fainting, despair; despairing, yield thy breath!

  (To RICHMOND.)
  I died for hope ere I could lend thee aid:
  But cheer thy heart, and be thou not dismay'd:
  God and good angel fight on Richmond's side;
  And Richard falls in height of all his pride.

(The GHOSTS vanish. KING RICHARD III starts out of his dream.)

ABOUT THE EDITORS

Lisa Bansavage is an actress whose career comprises Broadway, Off Broadway, regional theater, film, television, and national commercial credits, including *Master Class*, *Law and Order: Criminal Intent*, *The French Lieutenant's Woman*, *A Man for All Seasons*, *The Grapes of Wrath*, *Grace & Glory*, *Mastergate*, *Red Scare on Sunset*, *The Changeling*, *The Country Wife*, *A View from the Bridge*, *The Beauty Queen of Leenane*, *The Sisters Rosenweig*, *Night of the Iguana*, *A Time to Kill*, *Married to the Mob*, *Three Men and a Baby*, *The Fisher King*, *Diary of Anne Frank*, *Vampire Lesbians of Sodom*, *The Loman Family Picnic*, and a third of the full Shakespearean canon as well as a role opposite Sir Anthony Quayle in the BBC-London production of *An Exchange of Gifts*. She is a graduate of Carnegie-Mellon University's theater conservatory and holds a Master's in Theatre from the University of Pittsburgh where she was a Merrill Fellow. Her Shakespearean stage credits include performances with Great Lakes Shakespeare Festival, New Jersey Shakespeare Festival, Alabama Shakespeare Festival, Three Rivers Shakespeare Festival, Riverside Shakespeare Festival, and the Triple T Theatre Company in a variety of roles: Titania in *A Midsummer Night's Dream* (three times), Kate in *The Taming of the Shrew* (twice), Beatrice in *Much Ado About Nothing* (twice), Desdemona, Emilia, and Bianca in *Othello*, Portia in *The Merchant of Venice*, Celia in *As You Like It*, Lady Capulet, Lady Montague, and The Nurse in *Romeo and Juliet*, Mistress Quickly in *Henry IV Part I*, Elizabeth in *Richard III,* and Viola in *Twelfth Night*.

L. E. McCullough, Ph.D. is an educator, playwright, composer, and ethnomusicologist whose studies in music and folklore have spanned cultures throughout the world. Dr. McCullough is the former administrative director of the Humanities Theatre Group at Indiana University–Purdue University at Indianapolis and current director of the Children's Playwriting Institute in Woodbridge, New Jersey. Winner of the 1995 Emerging Playwright Award for his stage play *Blues for Miss Buttercup*, he is the author of *The Complete Irish Tinwhistle Tutor, Favorite Irish Session Tunes, St. Patrick Was a Cajun, The Complete Irish Tinwhistle Tunebook* and *Whistle Around the World* and has performed on the soundtracks for the PBS specials *The West, Lewis and Clark,* and *Not for Ourselves Alone: The Story of Elizabeth Cady Stanton and Susan B. Anthony.* Since 1991 Dr. McCullough has received forty-six awards in thirty-one national literary competitions and has had poems and short stories published 181 times in ninety-two North American literary journals. His books for Smith and Kraus include: *Plays of the Songs of Christmas; Stories of the Songs of Christmas; Ice Babies in Oz*: *Original Character Monologues; Plays of America from American Folklore, vol. 1 and 2; Plays of the Wild West, vol. 1 and 2; Plays from Fairy Tales; Plays from Mythology; Plays of People at Work; Plays of Exploration and Discovery; Anyone Can Produce Plays with Kids; Plays of Ancient Israel; Plays of Israel Reborn; Ultimate Audition Book for Teens, vol. 2; Ultimate Audition Book for Pre-Teens; "Now I Get It!": 12 Ten-Minute Classroom Drama Skits for Elementary Science, Math, Language and Social Studies, vol. 1 and 2, Wild and Wacky Characters for Kids;* and *Software Solutions for the Successful Actor* (with Lisa Bansavage and Dan Jacoby).

Jill K. Swanson is an actor and teacher with the Austin Shakespeare Festival in Austin, Texas. Notable performances include Desdemona in *Othello*, Oberon in *A Midsummer Night's Dream,* Beatrice in *Much Ado About Nothing,* and Helena in *A Midsummer Night's Dream.* Ms. Swanson studied Shakespeare with Jean McDaniel at Florida State University, where her roles included Rosalind in *As You Like It*, Emilia in *Othello*, Hermione in *The Winter's Tale,* and Phebe in *As You Like It.* Nothing has taught her more about performing Shakespeare than teaching kids for Austing Shakespeare Festival, St. Stephen's Episcopal School's Arts on the Lake program.